TEMPORARY HUSBAND

Kate had been forced into marrying
Blake Templeton, the film director,
and going on location with him. But
how could she stay with him, when he
was so cold towards her—and she loved
another man?

TEMPORARY HUSBAND

BY
SUSAN ALEXANDER

MILLS & BOON LIMITED
15–16 BROOK'S MEWS
LONDON W1A 1DR

*First published in Great Britain 1985
by Mills & Boon Limited*

© Susan Alexander 1985

*Australian copyright 1985
Philippine copyright 1985
This edition 1985*

ISBN 0 263 75002 7

*Set in Monophoto Plantin 11 on 11 pt.
01–0485 – 48890*

*Made and printed in Great Britain by
Richard Clay (The Chaucer Press) Ltd,
Bungay, Suffolk*

CHAPTER ONE

THE large black Rolls-Royce slid silently through the grey stone gateposts of the cemetery, slowly gathering speed as it moved out into the traffic on the main road.

In one corner of the back seat Kate Howard sat bolt upright, her set face a white blur behind the heavy black veil. Her eyes were riveted to the back of the grey uniformed chauffeur beyond the glass partition, but she saw nothing of the reality around her, her mind fixed on the finality of the scene she had just left. Over and over, like an endlessly repeated newsreel she could see the fresh earth fall into the open grave, gradually hiding the coffin from view and eventually covering it, burying it for ever.

It was over.

The phrase beat into her brain, reverberating round in her head, meaningless, hopeless and final.

The tall dark man at her side was also motionless, his face revealing nothing of his thoughts or feelings, his head turned away from his companion, his eyes on the rain hissing quietly against the tinted windows of the car.

As the Rolls ate up the miles into London, Kate's mind began to thaw, her tenacious self-control relaxing its hold. The past twenty-four hours had been a nightmare of frenzied activity, holding emotion at bay, firmly repressing pain and grief.

*   *   *

The telegram had arrived during one of her art classes, and they had tried to break it to her gently. Did she know her father was ill? Had she realised his health was deteriorating? But she had guessed almost at once, breaking out into hysterics, only to be heavily sedated. In the morning she had woken, her mind clear, her feelings frozen, and organised her journey home in time for the funeral. Her goodbyes to friends and teachers at her Paris finishing school had been oddly final, as though it was unlikely she would ever see them again.

Only Henri had refused to accept her outward coldness, her lack of any emotion. Within an hour of her 'phone call he had appeared at the school demanding to accompany her to London. Driving her to the airport he had argued and pleaded, but she had been firm. It was better she go alone.

And now she wondered if her departure would change their plans. For months they had been hoping for an invitation to Kate from the powerful old lady who had brought him up and still held the purse strings of the du Bois vineyard fortune that would come to Henri as the only male heir. Kate had met Henri's sister and brother-in-law one evening at their Paris house, and the obvious wealth and pride of the aristocratic du Bois family had kept her tongue-tied during the long meal. She had found nothing in common with their talk of horse racing, yachting, French politics and the glittering programme of entertainments and sports with which they seemed to fill their days. But Henri had felt quite differently about the success of the evening.

'They liked you, *chérie*' he said happily as he drove her home.

She laughed nervously. 'I don't see how they could. I never said a word.'

'They were interested in only one thing tonight.'

'And what was that?'

'Whether you are a virgin,' he answered bluntly.

She had blushed faintly in the darkness of the car.

'It is the thing of most importance' he insisted. 'Everything else is secondary.'

'But what about family, wealth, connections?' She'd spoken shyly. 'I don't belong to your world and they must have seen that.'

'When we marry' he said importantly, 'I will bring you into my world, and they will accept you. Anyway it is only grandmère who matters.'

'Have you spoken to her yet?' she asked anxiously.

'Er . . . no, not yet.' He hesitated. 'The time has to be right. Now that Gabrielle and Pierre have met you, it will be easier to approach grandmère. Next week I will go to the château. She can talk to me about wine and will be pleased with me for coming. That will be a good time. You will see. Everything will be fine.'

He flashed her a smile, showing white teeth in a handsome face. They kissed a lingering good night and, as always, she thrilled in his arms. Henri kissed her intimately and firmly, and had taught her to return his kiss. But he never lost control. Other boys with whom she had gone out in London had handled her clumsily and soon lost control, demanding responses she had no wish to give. But then Henri was much older than anyone else she knew. He was nearly twenty-four and, as her friend Mary always said, French boys grew up much faster and knew a lot more than English boys of the same age.

Following that evening Henri had been away a month while she wavered between anger that he didn't write and despair that she might never see him again. Finally, one morning a note arrived asking her to meet him. It had been snowing and Paris was white and frosty as she slithered in her heavy suede boots along the iced pavements to Notre-Dame.

He had taken her in his arms and kissed her, his face and lips cold against her skin. In the church they talked, sitting in a side chapel, whispering.

'Where have you been?' she began. 'Why didn't you write?'

'It wasn't possible, *chérie*. Please don't waste time talking about things that are not important.'

Kate looked at him. He was just the same. The regular features, blue eyes with pale straight brows, the full mouth and the skin tanned as always. The slim figure visible under the fur-lined coat was clad in immaculate twill trousers and light sports jacket. He was talking persuasively.

'I had to stay, *mon ange*, to win her round.' He reached for her hand and carried it to his lips. 'Did you miss me?' She melted at his touch. Perhaps he was sometimes thoughtless, but she did love him.

'Grandmère has agreed you may come and visit. So we go in the summer. She asks only you bring a girlfriend, to make it all respectable.' He laughed. 'Isn't that good? Aren't you pleased? Why do you look so solemn, like a . . . how you say . . . owl?'

At that she burst out laughing. 'Oh, Henri, you are funny.' And she had been all eagerness at his plans. 'I'll ask Mary. She'll enjoy it.'

'As long as she is prepared to be much alone, so that we can be together, I do not mind who it is.'

Kate hesitated. 'Well, she's not very well off, you know, and it will be a great treat for her. So we must be nice and show her round.'

'*Oui, bien, sûr* . . . of course.' He snapped his fingers. 'And now, *mon ange*, that is enough talk. Let us get out of here. I have not yet kissed you.'

And the invitation had arrived, embossed, heavily crested, and strangely forbidding. A month away. That's when she was due to go.

'We're here.'

The voice penetrated Kate's musings and she turned to her companion, still gripped by her memories, for a moment unsure of her surroundings. But it was not Henri's voice that spoke, nor his face at her side.

It was Blake. He was standing by the car, his hand held out to help her. She touched the hand briefly and walked past him into the house. In the hall she stood for a moment as though waiting . . . for the door to open to the study, for her father to appear. Almost she could hear his voice: 'Hello, sweetheart.'

But then the reality came crashing into her mind. Never again would he be there, welcoming, affectionate . . .

Blake touched her elbow, and she became

aware of voices behind the closed double doors of the living room. Awkwardly she turned away from Blake.

'I'm going up for a quick wash' she murmured and walked upstairs. In her room she took off her veil, wondering suddenly if it had been Blake who had organised everything ... the funeral, invitations, the sherry and biscuits that no doubt Mrs Buss was serving downstairs. Was it Blake, she tried to recall, who had sent the telegram?

Walking back downstairs she found Blake waiting in the hall. Her face softened. He was probably the only person who would understand how she felt. He had been her father's best friend for as long as she could remember. And over the years there had been countless occasions when she had been excited because he was taking her to a film première, the private view of a new art exhibition or merely a dawn gallop along Rotten Row in Hyde Park.

He was looking up at her and she realised they hadn't seen each other for nearly two years, years in which she had learnt to dress with Parisian chic, have her hair styled and use make-up. She must seem quite a stranger.

'Blake.'

She moved to kiss him as she always did, but he held her firmly at arms' length, his fingers hard on the silky material of her sleeves. Anxiously she looked up at him, her eyes questioning the rejection.

'The day isn't over yet,' he said coolly. 'Come along.' He was right. This was not the time for nostalgia. She drew away from him and walked towards the living room.

Conversation stopped abruptly as she entered,

and all eyes turned to her, more people in the room than she'd expected. For the first time her Paris training came to her aid. 'Feelings are private,' Madame always stressed, 'not for public display.' Her lips curved into a polite smile, she moved forward to greet her guests.

An hour later she was alone and exhausted. Reaction was beginning to set in, the large sherry she had sipped on an empty stomach making her feel slightly queasy. She'd find Mrs Buss and get herself something to eat. As she crossed the hall the doorbell rang, and Charles walked past her to open it, while she hurried to the back of the house, unwilling to cope with any more visitors.

'Kath.'

Kate stopped. Only one person ever called her that. She felt a sudden urge to run and hide from that voice she hadn't heard in four long years. Instead she turned and faced her mother.

The front door stood open, and the outline of her mother's figure showed clearly against the light streaming into the dark hall. Slowly they walked towards each other.

'You're too late' Kate said loudly into the void between them. Charles closed the door and walked past her.

'I'll bring some coffee,' he said quietly.

'I'll need something stronger than coffee.' Her mother had heard him. 'I hope you still keep the drinks where they used to be.' She walked into the living room and Kate followed.

As always, her mother's presence was overpowering. Kate remembered again the desperate years of her childhood with its constant fears of rejection because she was never the daughter her mother wanted ... pretty, neat, clean and feminine, to be shown off to neighbours and friends. She always chose the wrong moment to come tearing in, noisy, untidy and heedless of the stable odours she brought with her. Yet how ardently she had tried to be what her mother wanted, dressing in the frills and pastel shades she hated, ready and eager to please. But somehow, within minutes, there was always something outside that beckoned, or, ignored by her mother's friends, she would lie down on the floor with paper and crayons.

Even now Kate could feel the familiar dry throat, the sickness in the pit of her stomach and the sense of inadequacy. It all returned with the full force of childhood passion as her mother faced her, looking her up and down, measuring, evaluating.

'Well.' Bella Howard contemplated her daughter, eyes narrowed in her beautiful face. 'Widow's weeds?' she asked sweetly. 'You look like the widow rather than the daughter.'

Kate didn't say anything. Her mother was still incredibly beautiful. Blonde hair, blue eyes, the small pointed face still flawless. She was elegantly dressed in a fine wool suit, tailored to hint at the curves under its severity, the collar of a cream chiffon blouse cascading from her throat, legs superbly sheathed in silk, tiny feet in handmade leather. The familiar heavy perfume was already beginning to saturate the room.

Abruptly Kate turned away, walking to the french windows, her mind rejecting her mother's presence as she remembered painfully the last time she had seen her father.

It had been Easter and he had come to visit her in Paris. They had laughed and joked as always, and he had seemed less unhappy. Only at the end of their time together he had touched on the subject always near the surface of his mind.

'I don't suppose' he had asked casually, 'you've heard from your mother?'

She had shaken her head.

'I just wondered. Nothing important.'

He had kissed her and gone back to London, to die . . . alone, still as desperately in love with her mother as on the day she had left him four years earlier. And he had waited with his memories, hoping always that she would return to him . . . one day.

In the early months after she had gone, Kate had drawn very close to her father. He had kept her by his side, her bedtimes elastic as a series of housekeepers came and went, unable to cope with the half-child, half-mistress of the house she had become at thirteen.

But in the end, when she was fourteen, he had sent her away to school, and the separations had begun. She had tried to stop him, crying, cajoling, threatening, but he had been quietly firm. And she had loathed boarding school. The girls in her class had wasted no time on a new pupil intruding into the closed community formed when they were all much younger. And she had made no friends, living only for the end of each term and the moment she was free to rush headlong down the steps where Charles was waiting to drive her home.

But home, too, had changed. The farm and the horses had been the first to go. It had distressed her at the time, but she had asked no questions, fearing to trespass on her father's deepest emotions. Then she noticed pictures moved wider apart to cover spaces where some were missing. Finally, one Christmas, she had been shocked to see the half-empty cabinet housing her father's priceless Ming collection. And this time she found the courage to talk to him.

'Dad' she had begun awkwardly.

'Mm . . .' He'd been reading.

'I don't want anything for Christmas this year,' she had explained importantly.

'Good heavens, why ever not?' He had looked up in surprise.

'And I'm taking a holiday job in one of the big stores.'

'What's this all about?' His curiosity had been genuine.

'Nothing special.' She had been evasive.

'Come on, out with it.' He laughed. 'You want something so outrageously expensive you're softening me up for the kill.'

'Of course not.' She had been appalled.

At her expression his smile faded. 'You'd better tell me all about it,' he suggested quietly.

'Are we . . . short of money?' she blurted out and watched his face flush with embarrassment.

She had rushed across the room to him, burying her face against his chest, babbling incoherently.

'I'm sorry. I know it's none of my business.' She gulped. 'But I could leave school and look after you. Then we'd save the fees and we could let Mrs Buss go. I don't mind being poor.' She had finished and burst into tears.

For a moment he had stiffened. Then he put her away from him, calmly and deliberately as he did everything, pressing a large handkerchief into her hands.

'I think, young lady, it's time we had a talk,' he said firmly. 'You're growing up and I tend to forget it.' He smiled down at her. 'Come up here and sit beside me.'

They had settled on the sofa in front of the fire and he began to talk, slowly, hesitantly.

'I have to go back rather a long way ... to explain it all, to the time before you were born. When I met your mother I was thirty-eight and she was sixteen.' He coloured slightly and she looked away from him into the fire. 'I was experienced, relatively wealthy and probably appeared rather glamorous to her. I was certainly the only grown man she knew. Her other friends were all lads of her own age.' He cleared his throat.

'We fell in love and were married on her seventeenth birthday. Looking back I've thought many times I did her an injustice when I married her. She was too young to choose her own future. But I cared only that we loved each other, certain that we would continue to be happy together.' He paused, his eyes pensively on the fire. 'Her restlessness began when she reached thirty. It was some kind of threshold in her mind, and she started to wonder about all the things she'd never had, never tried. I let her do as she pleased, confident she needed to indulge her curiosity and would return to me.' He paused painfully.

'But I was wrong, and in the end she wanted to go. I understood, and she went with my blessing. She had given me years of happiness, perhaps more than I deserved for tying her down so young.'

Kate sat quite still, listening to the strong emotion in his voice, waiting for him to continue.

'Naturally when she went she needed money,' he said quietly, 'and I've tried to supply that. Unfortunately my earning days are coming to an end. But I've invested wisely and can now use my assets. I don't care a jot about my art collection, and your college fees are invested in a trust for you. But, sadly, antiques don't last for ever, and my worry is what will happen to her when I'm gone.'

He looked down at her, his eyes suddenly alight with hope. 'But by then, who knows, perhaps she will have tired of her wandering and come home again.'

Kate threw her arms round his neck. 'Thank you for telling me,' she whispered.

'I'm the lucky one, of course,' he said seriously. 'I have you.'

The first sign of trouble came only months later. They were at breakfast, Kate remembered, and it was half term. It was snowing and the soft flakes whirled against the window panes, the trees in the square black and bare. Her father was going through his post when he cried out suddenly, and she looked up to see his face rigid with shock.

'What is it? What's happened?' She had shown her agitation.

He didn't speak, searching in his waistcoat pocket for his pills. She ran for some water and watched the blue tension round his mouth as he swallowed the pills and they began to take effect.

Her mother wanted a divorce, he explained haltingly. She wished to marry again.

Since that day Kate had hated her mother with single-minded ferocity as she watched her father lose all hope, all will to live. And now he was dead, killed by her mother as surely as if she had taken a gun and shot him.

Charles appeared with coffee and biscuits.

'Thank you' her mother smiled archly, and he nodded and left them.

'Well, puss,' Bella Howard splashed soda into her whisky, 'you haven't changed. Still that sour, disapproving, puritanical expression with which you were born.'

'Why didn't you come to the funeral?' Kate asked ignoring the gibe.

'My dear, I couldn't. I would have wept and disgraced you all.' She looked at her daughter standing frozen and rigid. 'I'm sure you didn't weep'.

'So why are you here?'

'Well,' her mother began and stopped. 'Please come and sit down, Kath. This isn't going to be easy.'

Reluctantly Kate turned away from the window and sat primly on the edge of a chair, her knees pressed together, her hands clasped. Her mother brought her glass and sat opposite.

'Did you know your father and I were reconciled . . . at the end?' she asked.

'I don't believe it,' Kate said bluntly.

Bella Howard tensed. 'Look', she said forcefully, 'I don't like this any more than you, but it has to be got through somehow. So let's try and be civilised about it.' She leaned back. 'I know you think I hate you, but I don't. I never did. It's just that . . . I never wanted children. I warned your father, but he didn't take it seriously.'

The two women sat tense, their eyes locked, a certain defiance in the older woman's eyes, cold emptiness in her daughter's gaze. Kate was determined not to break down in front of her mother. Clenching her hands in her lap, she schooled her features to show nothing of the sick hatred inside her.

'I came home,' her mother began again, 'to be with your father . . . at the end.'

'So what happened to your new husband?' Kate interrupted rudely. 'Did he come too?'

'Stop it!' Her mother was angry. Getting up she poured herself another drink, then walked to the window, her back to the room.

'My marriage . . . didn't quite work out,' she said heavily. 'Your father knew all about that and was happy to . . . see me at the end.'

Kate bit her lips hard. Was this why she had been kept away? Had he not wished to antagonise her mother by sending for his daughter? Kate's head was beginning to throb with tension, and she hoped her mother would finish quickly what she had come to say. Bella Howard came back and sat down.

'Did you know your father had money worries in the last years?' she asked next.

'If you mean did I know he had to sell his art collection to finance your lifestyle, yes I did know.'

'Is there no end to your impertinence?' Bella turned a furious face to her daughter. 'Will you control your tongue and listen to me?'

'You're asking the questions,' Kate pointed out coldly.

'Very well. I've tried to meet you halfway, but it seems you're too childish to appreciate it. You always were immature for your age. So now I'll give it to you straight.' She breathed deeply.

'Your father and I discussed his problems and your future to find a solution.'

'My future's settled,' Kate interrupted again. 'I'm going to art school when I finish in Paris.'

'No, you're not. That's no longer possible.'

'Why not?'

'Because there's no money,' Bella said bluntly.

'The money's been invested for me ... in a trust!' Kate objected. Bella Howard ignored her daughter's statement.

'For the past three years your father has been living in debt, and now there's nothing left. The rest of the art collection is mortgaged, so is this house. He's left us with colossal debts and nothing to live on,' she finished dully.

The room was suddenly quiet, heavy with foreboding, and Kate sat stunned, unable to grasp fully what her mother had said. Restlessly she got up and moved back to the window. Outside it was raining heavily now, water splashing against the windows, sweeping like tears down the glass. The grave would be soaked, she thought suddenly, the flowers dying in the onslaught of water. Grief rose unexpectedly in her mind like a cloud, but she closed her eyes fiercely against it. There would be plenty of time for grieving. Behind her Bella continued tonelessly.

'Your father and I talked it all out, and in the end there seemed to be only one solution.'

Kate turned back to face the room.

'We decided . . .' Bella hesitated, avoiding her daughter's eyes. 'We agreed it would be best to arrange a marriage with someone who could look after us both and cope with the debts.'

'An arranged marriage for whom?' Kate asked caustically, 'You?'

'No, of course not.' Her mother blushed, her eyes down. 'For you.'

'How fascinating.' Kate drawled sarcastically. 'So do tell me, mother, to whom have you decided to sell me?'

There was a long silence while Bella Howard said nothing. Then she spoke.

'Blake Templeton,' she said in a hushed whisper.

The quiet room was suddenly filled with Kate's hysterical laughter, her voice rising loud and shrill as her control snapped.

'Stop it, Kate.'

'Oh, but it's so funny. Don't you see, mother, how hilarious it is? For a moment I thought all this was serious. I didn't realise it was all a joke. You should have told me.'

'Hysterics won't help,' her mother said coldly. 'And it's no joke. I wish it was,' she added quietly. 'Blake has been financing your father for several years. The house is his and so is the rest of the art collection. Lately he's been paying for your schooling, the servants, cars, me ... everything.'

Kate's eyes widened with shock and she sat down heavily, the room suddenly deathly quiet.

'Blake and your father have been seeing a lot of each other,' Bella continued in a low monotone. 'In the end they made this strange agreement. Discussing it with me was only a formality. When I got here your father had already decided.'

Kate made an effort to pull herself together, forcing her mind to function.

'And what exactly is the agreement?' she asked unsteadily.

'Blake will finance your schooling and my ...

me, on the understanding that you two are married.' The older woman swallowed painfully, still avoiding her daughter's eyes. 'If you refuse, there'll be no money. We'll be penniless and in debt to Blake.' She paused. 'The will gives Blake your father's consent to the marriage because you're under age. I've had it checked, and Sherwood assures me it's valid.'

'Sherwood?'

'Your father's solicitor.'

'But it doesn't make sense.' Kate was trying to reason it out. 'We know Blake's got so much money he wouldn't notice what we cost him. So, if he's going to waive the debts and finance us, why the marriage?'

Her mother looked down into her glass and didn't reply.

'Mother, you know what nonsense it is.' Kate tried to keep the panic out of her voice. 'Blake doesn't want to marry me. He doesn't want to marry anyone. Even before I could understand what it was all about, Blake and his women were a family joke. Don't you remember?' she insisted urgently. 'There was no reason why Blake should marry because he had the pick of the world's most beautiful women any time he wanted ... without marriage.'

'I know,' Bella said quietly. 'But you don't seem to realise how lucky you are. Any other woman would give her back teeth to marry Blake.'

'Well any other woman can have him,' Kate said angrily, fear momentarily forgotten. 'He must be old enough to be my father. For year's he's been a sort of uncle to me. And now you're surprised I won't fall into his arms. It's obscene and I won't do it.'

'Don't be ridiculous he's only thirty-six, that's young enough, besides you have no choice,' her mother said coldly.

'Oh, yes, I have,' Kate shouted at her, 'what you don't know is that I can't marry Blake. I can't marry anyone because I'm engaged to be married to someone else.'

A slight sound stopped both women. As her mother looked up nervously, Kate whirled round.

Standing in the doorway was Blake Templeton.

CHAPTER TWO

'BLAKE, thank goodness . . .'

Impetuously Kate moved towards him, holding out her hands, knowing he would dispel the nightmare her mother had evoked. But as she reached him she noticed his eyes were cold, his smile formal and impersonal. She stopped as her hands began to tremble and Blake walked past her into the room.

'Bella.' He bowed politely to her mother. 'Drink?' He picked up the decanter and held it out, refilling her mother's glass before helping himself. Then he walked over to the fireplace and turned to face them both.

'You were saying, Kate?' he asked smoothly.

'I . . . no, it doesn't matter. Another time. I think I'll go up now.' She turned away from the coldness in his face. 'No doubt I'll see you both tomorrow.'

'You'll see me tonight,' he said coolly, 'we're having dinner. I'll pick you up at eight.'

'Oh, no . . . I mean' she corrected herself hastily, 'I've . . . I don't want to see anyone tonight, thank you.'

'You and I will talk this evening. It can't wait till tomorrow.' His voice was inflexible.

'Leave the child,' Bella said sharply, 'if she doesn't want to go out. Explanations can wait till tomorrow.' Blake didn't move or glance at her mother.

'Tomorrow we have the reading of the will,' he said, 'it'll have to be tonight.'

He sat down facing the fire, long legs stretched out, and Kate was relieved to escape his searching gaze.

'Before you go, Kate, please finish what you were telling your mother.'

'No, Blake, not now.'

'Now, Kate,' he said quietly. 'Your mother's told you about your father's problems and his agreement with me?'

'Yes.' She sat down away from him and noticed her mother looking at Blake with a strange entreaty. 'I . . . I was telling mother,' Kate went on haltingly, 'I'm not free to marry. I'm engaged and we're going to be married as soon as I'm of age.'

'Du Bois?' Blake's voice was cold.

Kate's startled glance rested on his profile. 'How did you know?'

'You will not marry him,' Blake said flatly.

Kate raised her head in anger. 'You have no right or power to stop me,' she said resolutely, trying to match the indifference of his tone.

'You're mistaken. I have both the right and the power.' He didn't glance round at her. 'And now upstairs to bed. I've asked Mrs Buss to bring you some food, and I'll see you later,' he said dismissively.

Kate got up. 'I don't know what this is all about or what game you're playing, but I'm not ruining my life for anyone . . . or anything. And no one's going to make me do something I don't want,' she ended heatedly.

'No one's asking you to ruin your life,' he said shortly. 'And now upstairs before you fall down and have to be carried.'

Her colour high she turned and fled from them

both, her throat locked, her eyes strained with
unshed tears.

Kate peered into the mirror. Her make-up was
too heavy. She had kept adding more, hoping to
hide the pallor and droop of her face. Picking up
a tissue she began to cleanse and start again.
Touching her lips lightly with gloss and
smoothing a clear foundation into her skin, she
threw her robe on to the bed and took the long
black velvet skirt from its hanger. Together with
a black satin blouse the outfit suited her mood,
black pearl studs in her ears the only ornament.

Her thick chestnut hair she wore as always in a
heavy fall almost to her shoulders, two tortoise-
shell combs keeping the weight off her face. The
large, widely spaced dark blue eyes had a slightly
clouded look, and the mouth without colour
looked oddly vulnerable, the full finely moulded
lips pale and soft. But the straight nose and
firmly rounded chin were familiar as always, no
outward sign of the inner turmoil of the day.

The bell pealed at the front door.

A quick spray of her new French perfume, her
short velvet jacket over her arm, a black
embroidered evening bag and she was ready.

Blake was waiting in the hall and she looked
down into his face, anxiously trying to gauge his
mood, unaware of the picture she made at the top
of the stairs, a tall slim figure in satin and velvet,
the fiery hair gleaming under the chandelier. She
sensed a faint tension in his face as she met the
hard grey eyes watching her, a glitter in their
depth.

'Hello, kitten,' he said softly.

She smiled at the familiar endearment, running

down happily as she felt the tension ease between them.

'Let's go,' he said and held out his hand for her jacket. In silence they walked out into the damp evening, the trees in the square still dripping with rain, the old-fashioned street lamps throwing pools of light into the black puddles on the pavement. Blake opened the door of a maroon coloured Bentley Continental which Kate didn't recognise, and within minutes they were on their way to the West End.

The restaurant was full and noisy as they followed the headwaiter to a corner table. Kate looked round at famous faces and beautifully dressed women, her eyes glazed with pain as she remembered it was still the day of her father's funeral, and here she was, dining out, as though it had never happened.

A strange sense of unreality stole over her. Even Blake seemed unreal. He was ordering, frowning down at the wine list while the waiter wrote busily.

Suddenly there was a shriek above the hum of voices.

'Blake . . . darling! Is it really you?'

A woman rushed up to Blake and kissed him passionately on the mouth. For a moment they were intent on each other, and Kate watched as he responded to the woman's kiss. At last they separated and Blake rose to make introductions, murmuring 'Blanche Dumont' which meant nothing to Kate.

The woman was stunning. Raven-haired, liquid blue eyes and a dazzling white skin, she was strikingly dressed in emerald chiffon that wafted round her superb figure. As they talked Kate looked at Blake.

It was nearly two years since she had seen him, and he probably hadn't changed much in that time. It was she who had altered. As she'd told her mother, to her Blake had always been an uncle figure whose affection she took for granted and whose teasing made her laugh. If she'd thought about him at all, she would have felt she could go to him if ever she was in trouble. But tonight she was seeing him for the first time as a person . . . a man.

He wasn't handsome like Henri. Blake was tall, broad and muscular with wide shoulders and long legs. A square face with deep-set light grey eyes was darkly tanned and topped by crisp black hair cut close to the head and growing down to the collar, short sideburns tinged with silver. Looking down at the woman by his side, his face was creased with amusement, wide lips curved into a teasing smile.

No, Kate mused, not handsome, but forceful and assured, a certain charisma emanated from him and a sexual magnetism that was strongly virile, a challenge to any female. Was he also cold? For the first time she wondered why he had never married. The story went that he had affairs with the leading ladies in the films he directed. Since a film tended to occupy him for about a year, most of the ladies lasted that long. And gossip claimed they stayed with him only on his terms, sharing nothing but his bed, were permitted no influence on his lifestyle.

In the past she had laughed thinking . . . good old Blake, there goes another one. But now she shivered. What was it like for the women he discarded? Did they give themselves to him only to find he became bored and rejected their love?

He was ruthless, only she'd never noticed, never had to face it. And now she had to persuade him to let her marry Henri. And she was afraid of what he might do . . . to her life, her feelings.

'Kate, did you hear me?' Blake's voice was sharp, and she looked up to find him staring down at her intently.

She stood up. 'I'm not all that well, Blake. I think I'll go home.'

'No.' He put out a hand, then turned to the other woman. 'Please forgive us, Blanche, but Kate isn't too well. Another night perhaps.'

'Darling, what a shame,' Blanche purred, reaching up to touch her lips to his cheek. 'Is she just young or is she jealous?'

Kate's lips set angrily as the other woman left them.

'Sit down, Kate,' Blake said curtly, 'you're making an exhibition of yourself.'

'How dare you, Blake Templeton.' She was incredulous. 'You know perfectly well every woman in the room has been drinking in your performance.'

'That's better,' he said calmly, 'we seem to be communicating again. Whatever were you thinking about? You looked as though you'd gone into a trance.'

Just then the food arrived and Kate realised she was hungry. Blake had ordered all the things she liked, and she began to unwind as she tucked into her escalope of veal à la crème, and made no further conversation. His face, too, looked more relaxed as they finished the last of their wine and coffee arrived.

'I'm not ordering liqueurs,' he said quietly.

'We've a lot of talking to do and you're tired enough as it is.'

Kate looked down into the blackness of her coffee and her throat locked, the wetness of tears on her lashes. Blake asked for the bill and a moment later he rose.

'Leave that,' he said curtly, 'we can have some more later.'

In the car she sat silent and tense. Neither spoke until Blake switched off the engine.

'Where are we?' she asked.

'We're going up to my flat. I'm not talking to you in public.'

She didn't resist when he took her arm and they walked into the stone-and-glass building. With a nod from Blake to the uniformed porter they entered the lift. As it hissed quietly to a stop, Blake unlocked a second door and Kate found herself in the large hallway of his home. In the dark he took her through into the living room, and she gasped in surprise.

The room was dominated by long windows running the width of two walls. Through these, white-barked beeches and leafy chestnuts rising from their roots in Regents Park below shimmered in the moonlight, filling the unlit room with a ghostly panoply of luminous green.

'Blake, it's fabulous,' she breathed. 'Please don't turn on the light.'

He laughed lightly. 'Just a small one so we don't bump into the furniture.'

A soft diffused spot lit up a slender satinwood table, holding drinks and a coffee-maker.

'Coffee?'

'No, thanks, nothing for me.' As her eyes became accustomed to the dim light Kate looked round. A huge leather-topped Edwardian desk stood against one wall, strewn with papers and open books. Opposite hung a collection of old theatre prints and posters, their slim gold frames gleaming faintly in the half dark. Low bookcases ran beneath the windows the full length of both walls, and a thick Chinese wash carpet in brilliant blues and cream almost covered the polished wooden floor. Several starkly modern chrome-and-black leather chairs were grouped round two low coffee tables.

Kate sat down carefully to find the strangely shaped chair hugged and supported with surprising comfort, the stylish warmth of the room enfolding her with its unobtrusive elegance.

'Blake?' she began haltingly, 'were you with father . . . at the end?'

'Yes.'

'Did he say anything, anything special?'

'That's one of the things we're going to talk about.' He brought his drink and sat opposite, stretching long legs out in front of him. 'Your father was a very worried man at the end,' he said quietly, his hands cupping the brandy glass, his eyes on the amber liquid. 'He was concerned about you, of course, but his most important worry was your mother, and this you must understand. You're young and strong, but your mother is not, and she's never been trained to work. During the last weeks this became an obsession with him.'

'Why didn't you let me know?' she cried out in confusion. 'Why didn't someone send for me? I can't understand how you could have been so cruel. You must have known I'd want to be with him. Oh, God, I wish I'd died, too.'

'Stop it, Kate. That's childish and you're going to have to put childish things behind you. I wanted to send for you,' he went on after a moment, 'but your father wouldn't have it. He was adamant you were to be told nothing and he didn't want you here.' He lifted his head and looked across at her. 'Not because he didn't love you, but because he couldn't face telling you what he'd arranged for your future. He knew well enough how you'd feel about that.'

She put her head down into her hands, trying hard not to give way to the despair that was washing through her.

'Take your time,' Blake said quietly, 'I'll answer any questions fully and completely.'

'Thank you,' she whispered. 'I'm trying to keep calm.'

'I know,' he said gently.

'Do you?' she asked. 'Can you understand what it means to me?'

'I think so, Kate. I've known you a long time.'

'So will you tell me now what it is he wanted me to do?' He got up and moved to the windows, but didn't answer immediately. The silence was so prolonged that Kate lifted her head and looked at him. He was lost in thought and the grim set of his lips, the clenched jaw, indicated those thoughts were not happy ones.

'We agreed in the end the only solution was for us to be married,' he said heavily. 'That way I can take care of your mother and you'll be protected.'

Kate felt the hysteria rise in her throat as he confirmed what her mother had told her. Putting up a hand across her eyes she swallowed hard.

'B ... but ... but ...' she managed at last, 'why ...'

'Stop it, Kate,' he said again. 'You have nothing to fear, not from the arrangement with your father or from marriage with me.'

'But, Blake,' she was concentrating fiercely, trying to master her voice, 'it's all such nonsense. You know you don't want to marry me. I'm young, and unsophisticated, not glamorous or famous as your girlfriends always are.' She paused awkwardly. 'And you always said you would never marry because you couldn't be faithful to any woman for more than a year.'

He didn't reply, and she saw he was frowning heavily, his face in profile remote, his eyes fixed on the greenery beyond the windows.

'Let's leave my side for a moment, shall we?' he asked at last, his voice oddly harsh. 'Consider your father's reason for the arrangement. You're seventeen and need protection. For various reasons your mother can't give you that protection and I can. That's really all there is to it.'

'All?' She was panting now, anger and panic battling in her voice. 'If that's all, why do we have to get married? Why can't you be my guardian till I'm eighteen?'

'Cool down, Kate,' he commanded, 'you'll make yourself ill if you go on agonising like this. In three months you'll be eighteen certainly, but the situation won't have changed. There'll still be no money for your art school, your living or your mother.'

'But if you're paying for me to study, why can't you leave it at that? I'll have protection at college like any other student. I'll live in a hostel if that's what you want. I'll toe the line.'

'And what of holidays?'

'I can live here ... or the house if you're keeping it.'

'No, Kate, you couldn't live with me.' His lips curled. 'No doubt you think me as old as Methuselah, but I'm too young for us to live together.'

There was an awkward silence.

'All right,' she said evenly, 'then accept the alternative. I'm engaged to be married ... unofficially. As soon as we have the approval of Henri's grandmother, we can be married. Henri is very rich and you won't have to worry about me again.'

'No, Kate, it won't do.' He turned round to her. 'It's been a long day and I don't wish to prolong this, so please hear me out. When I've finished you can have your say.'

Impatiently he pushed his hands deep into his trouser pockets, his head thrust forward in thought. It was such a familiar posture and Kate remembered it so clearly from the past that she relaxed in her chair, prepared to listen.

'Your father and I agreed that a temporary marriage between us would give you the chance to bridge the gap between adolescence and maturity. We hoped to prevent your going into something ... irrevocable, that might make you unhappy, such as living with your mother, living alone or ... embarking on an early marriage. We were both aware of your interest in du Bois,' he added coldly.

Suddenly he turned sharply to face her. The light shone into his face and she could see clearly the empty controlled blankness of his eyes. As she caught her breath, he continued.

'Our marriage will take place in one week. It will be in form only and it will be temporary. Our relationship will remain as it has always been, and I hope we will continue to be friends.' He paused for a moment.

'I'm in the middle of a film. In three weeks I start location shooting in France and you will come with me. We'll spend the next six months together until you are due to start art school. If by that time you still wish to marry du Bois and he feels the same, I will arrange an annulment. If you no longer wish to marry him we'll continue with our marriage until I feel you're able to look after yourself or are ready to be married to someone else.'

Neither moved in the silence that followed. Kate was rigid with fear and helplessness. There seemed no words that could reach him, and she longed to scream and fight, to show him how much she hated what he was trying to do to her. Finally, she raised her head. His face was impassive, showing no thoughts or feelings, and from somewhere she found her cool.

'I find it difficult to believe you wish to marry me . . . on any terms. Surely my father was rather selfish to ask it of you? And perhaps you both misjudged me. You haven't seen me since I was sixteen. Things have changed and so have I.' She bit her lips, fearful of showing emotion, determined to remain calm and reasonable. 'I understand how you feel about Henri. But perhaps you could show me a little trust. Leave me in the house with Mrs Buss when you go to France. If you wish I'll have a girlfriend live with me and keep any other conditions you care to impose.' She swallowed painfully. 'But I can't marry you, Blake. I'm sorry. It's not possible . . . on any terms.'

Ignoring completely what she'd said, he turned away and began to speak, firmly, deliberately.

'This film is rather different from my usual comedies. It's a love story. The main character is a sculptor, and during the story she makes a bust of the man she loves. At the beginning his face eludes her and she destroys several attempts. Then she falls so wildly in love with him that she forgets all about work. In the end he deserts her, leaving her for another woman. And then she sculpts his head from memory, beautifully, lovingly, and it turns out to be the best thing she's ever done. But the likeness is so good, so true, that she can't bear to live with it because she longs for the original and grows to hate the bust.'

He turned sharply to face her. 'I'd like you to do the sculpting for me. It needs someone to be with us while we're shooting, to teach the actress how to use her hands, her tools, her materials. Do you think you could do that, Kate?'

'Oh, Blake,' she breathed, 'how could I refuse? It's the kind of challenge all artists dream about.' She spoke impulsively and as soon as she'd finished, she knew she'd made a mistake. A gleam of triumph glittered in the hard eyes and his mouth curled mockingly.

'Good' he said softly.

Clever, she thought, her mind searching for a response.

'And then I can be part of the unit,' she said casually, 'with a job on the picture, I'll be able to live with them.' She looked at him, wide-eyed, smiling, wondering if he would agree. But his face mocked her.

'No, Kate, the job is yours, but on my terms.'

'Blackmail?' Her eyes narrowed.

'Not at all,' he replied carelessly. 'You'll marry me in any case and come to France. But what you do there is up to you. If you accept the job, that's fine. If not, I'll find someone else.'

She bit her lip and tried to think, to find a way out. For the moment she would have to agree. Then, before the week was out, she would disappear, change her name and find a job. There could be no wedding without her presence.

'If you're thinking of running away,' he drawled, 'forget it. Ever since you went to Paris you've had someone keeping an eye on you, reporting back to me.'

She stared at him in horror. 'I don't believe it,' she whispered. 'How dare you invade my privacy and allow someone to play peeping Tom to my private life?' She was angry now, shaking with it. 'You disgust me, do you know that? I wouldn't marry you if you were the last man anywhere. You just don't understand ordinary people, do you? Your actresses lap you up and don't care how you treat them as long as they can be photographed with you ... Blake Templeton's latest.'

Her eyes wild, her breast heaving, she stormed at him, 'There are people, you know, who fall in love and get married and go on loving each other. If you're not one of them, that's too bad. But I am.' Her voice sank. 'I don't care about money, fame ... success. I just want to be with the man I love and have him care for me. I don't want to be with someone who takes out a temporary lease on me. I'm going to marry for love, as my father loved my mother.'

Her control finally broke and she put her hands to her face to stem the tears now streaming from her eyes, her sobs the only sound in the quiet room.

She looked up at last to see Blake standing stiff and rigid, strangely pale in the dim light, his eyes almost closed, the mouth grimly set. Compassion and contrition stabbed her.

'Blake, I'm sorry . . . I didn't mean . . .'

His face lifted and the mouth curled into a self-mocking smile. Her breath caught as she saw the deep, bleak emptiness of his eyes. What had she said? She got up and held out her hands.

'Forgive me, Blake, please . . .'

He caught her as she reached him and his fingers bit hard into her shoulders, holding her away from him. She stood in his grip, miserable and contrite, the tears still streaming down her face.

Briefly she heard him exclaim impatiently, and then she was in his arms, held close against his chest, sobbing incoherently. He didn't speak, but held her, letting her cry, one hand stroking the hair back from her face.

After a while her sobbing died down, and she was aware of a tension in his body, muscles tightly clenched as though exerting some unusual control. And a strange lethargy seemed to seep through her. She wanted to move closer, to melt into his arms and feel the warmth of him envelop her. They both stood quite still only just touching.

Then he moved abruptly, and her face suffused with colour, shyness and embarrassment keeping her tongue-tied. To cover her confusion she reached for her bag, searching for a tissue, unable to understand the strange thoughts and feelings that had rushed through her in Blake's embrace.

'Get your things, Kate. I'm driving you home,' he said coldly.

CHAPTER THREE

KATE stepped back from the bust and looked critically at the clay face on the pedestal. It was coming along quite well, she decided.

Sighing with satisfaction she stretched her aching arms, flexing her fingers to ease the muscles, and walked over to the sink to wash. Drying her hands she looked round the studio that had become virtually her home since her arrival in France three weeks earlier. Blake had made quite a ceremony of showing her round, bowing formally as he handed her the key, his eyes crinkling, the mouth curved in the familiar mocking grin.

'The key to your private retreat,' he had announced. It was beautiful. A five-sided pavilion like an old summer house, it was built of thick local stone, the walls rising to the low-slung roof, separate panes soaring to a pointed tip. Each window could be curtained off, giving light as needed at different times of the day. The inside was white, from the washed walls, linen curtains and deep leather sofas, to the tiled floor and immaculate shower room screened behind louvred doors. Tool racks lined the walls with trestle tables below, and in one corner a huge white porcelain sink held shelving for her clay.

'It's terrific, Blake,' she enthused. 'I don't know what to say. Thank you.'

'Glad you like it. Let me know if anything's missing.'

'I never dreamed you'd go to so much trouble.'

'Don't give it a thought,' he drawled, 'it was the brain child of the film's art director. We'll be doing all the close work in here and his design is intended to get the best natural light.'

'Oh.' Her smile had died and she'd felt exceedingly foolish. 'Of course.'

At that he'd turned, flicking her cheek with one finger. 'I did keep an eye on it, kitten. I knew you'd like it.'

And she had grinned back, sharing the joke, a sudden feeling of the old affection between them.

The last days in London had been packed with activity. Looking back she recognised Blake had kept it all deliberately light and business-like. They'd gone shopping for the clothes they'd need during the summer, and he had handled it all so casually they might have been together for years.

In the same mood they had dealt with the wedding itself. She hadn't bought a special outfit, wearing the simple coffee-and-cream linen suit in which she was to travel. Nor had they exchanged rings. The plain band he had chosen for her and the ceremony at the registry office with its total absence of any emotion, had seemed merely another of many business details. After the wedding they had collected their passports and lunched in one of Blake's favourite Soho restaurants before picking up their luggage and making their way out of London.

Arriving at the small airfield where Blake's Cessna jet waited for them, she had had her only moment of panic. As she watched her pigskin cases loaded side by side with his, labels crisp and new, 'Mrs K. Templeton', she had been overwhelmed

by a sudden sense of disaster. This was no
charade, no casual holiday from which she would
return to her normal life. This was marriage,
however odd and different. She was tied to Blake,
and however brief their marriage turned out to
be, he had rights over her that were not of her
own choosing, while the man she loved didn't
even know she'd deserted him. Rigid with shock
she stood staring as the luggage was stowed, her
eyes wide with fear, the casual pattern of the last
days suddenly falling into place.

'Kate.'

Blake's voice echoed distantly, but she took no
notice. He came down the steps and took her
arm, guiding her into the plane to one of the
comfortable day beds. He took off her shoes,
covering her with a light blanket, and she lay
back unresisting, her eyes on his face. She could
find no kindness there, no affection, and she
turned away, burying her face in the cushions
behind her head.

He woke her with coffee as they neared the
Mediterranean.

'Come on, sleepyhead, you don't want to miss
this,' he said lightly. Strapping her into the co-
pilot's seat, he took over the controls.

'See how you like it,' he grinned at her.

The excitement enmeshed her within minutes.
It was heady being in the cockpit with glass all
round giving a fantastic view, instead of the tiny
window of normal flights. She watched entranced
as the light plane dived at Blake's touch, coming
out of the clouds into brilliant sunshine, the dark
blue ribbon of the Rhône river far below,
winding its way into the distance.

'Oh Blake, it's magic.'

'I can see I'll have to teach you to fly,' he teased.
'Oh, yes, would you? I'd adore it.'

'Mm . . . perhaps.' His white teeth flashed as
he smiled, sharing her excitement. 'When the
film's finished.'

He recognised his mistake immediately and a
slight flush rose under his tan as the laughter
died out of her face. Mention of the film had
brought her back to reality, reminding Kate of
the life she was leaving behind, the future
planned for her so ruthlessly by the man at her
side. He turned away as constraint rose between
them to last for the rest of the journey.

Locking the studio Kate made her way through
the long grass to the edge of the cliff. The studio
stood high on the rocky promontory above the
curved bay that protected Blake's preciously
guarded privacy.

The gardens sloped steeply in a riot of
hibiscus, wild orchids, pink tamaris and spiky
dwarf palms lining the sandy path that wound
down to the beach. Two guest bungalows were
perched on the edge of the cliff enjoying
magnificent views out to sea while the main
house below was hidden from view in its own belt
of trees.

Here dazzling white walls enhanced the pale
brown of latticed shutters on the high windows of
the first floor, opening out on to a verandah that
ran the full length of the house. At ground level
floor-to-ceiling patio doors were shaded by silk
blinds protecting the interior from the heat. The
white stone terrace was covered with vines that
trailed across a white wooden trellis down pillars
to the edge of the pool.

Inside, the cool touched her like balm. High ceilings, white-washed walls and stone tiles under foot kept the temperature down. Huge stone winged fireplaces gave visions of log fires and the smell of wood on long winter evenings, and black wrought iron chandeliers with round pearly glass globes looked down on the red and gold of embroidered chairs and thickly cushioned sofas. The dining room was a stylish contrast with soft lemon walls and high-backed slender antique chairs set round the exquisite oval of the Sheraton table.

Upstairs, all was modernity with luxuriously fitted bathrooms, voile canopied beds and handwoven rugs covering the high gloss of darkly polished floors.

As Kate showered in her own bathroom, the silence of the villa all round, she thought about the evening ahead. Louis and his wife, Annabelle, ran the house impeccably to Blake's demands, serving superbly cooked food at any time she chose to appear, and seeing to her every comfort.

Blake she saw rarely. Occasionally she would hear voices and he would be there. Members of his crew would be with him and introduced. She had met Archie, the cameraman, and Tony, Blake's first assistant, but their cheerful voices always died to silence when she appeared. Then Blake would be affectionate with her, but she retreated rapidly, feeling unwanted, her presence an intrusion into their all-embracing film world. They would retire to Blake's study where Annabelle served drinks and snack meals, until they emerged again to roar off in their separate cars.

If Blake was in they shared a meal, and he

would enquire politely if she was well before disappearing into his study for the rest of the evening. The previous week he had informed her the rest of the crew had arrived and filming would begin within a matter of days.

'Quite a few of them are staying on the yacht,' he explained.

'The yacht?'

'My yacht. It's convenient and serves as a base for me. I've my office there, a cutting room and a small theatre.'

'Oh.'

'This place is my retreat,' he went on. 'Once we start shooting, I'm surrounded by people all day and most of the night. If I didn't have this place to come back to I'd go nuts.'

She looked at him blankly, trying to understand the seriousness of his tone.

'Have you read the script?' he asked abruptly.

'Yes.'

'Well?'

'I found it quite moving,' she said. 'It's a charged emotional subject, but it's been treated lightly and delicately.'

He looked up in surprise. 'That's remarkably acute.'

She flushed and looked down at her food.

'Do you understand how the sculpting fits into the story?'

'I think so.' She hesitated. 'But I won't have anything to do with all that, will I?'

'Mm . . .' He was looking at her rather intently and she wondered what he was thinking. 'I haven't decided yet how it's going to be handled. It depends on Blanche.'

'Blanche?'

'Blanche Dumont. You remember. We met her that night we ...' his voice died as they both remembered and Kate coloured. It had been the day of the funeral.

'Yes, I remember,' she said quietly. 'I didn't realise she was in the film.'

'Playing Laura she more or less is the film.'

'She's playing Laura?' Kate couldn't imagine the sleek, sophisticated woman she had met playing the pale, passionate and finally stricken Laura of the story.

'I'll have my work cut out getting the performance I want from her,' he said, 'that's why she'll be living here with us.'

'Living here?' Kate echoed.

'You're repeating everything I say.' Blake was irritated. 'Are you getting hard of hearing?' He looked across at her. 'Among other things she'll have to learn is how to handle the clay and tools. Teaching her that will be your job.'

'Oh, no, Blake, I couldn't ...' she objected nervously. 'How could I teach her when I'm learning myself? And someone as overwhelming as Miss Dumont. I really couldn't.'

'Stop gabbling, Kate. Certainly you'll do it, with tact and understanding. You know your craft and she doesn't. You'll only be teaching her the minimum for the role. You're not training her to be a sculptor. So please don't treat me to hysterics. I have enough of that on the picture already.'

She bit her lips.

'In any case we'll have Earl Holland here, and he's fun and relaxed, a real pro.'

'You mean Earl Holland, the film star?'

'Tell me, Kate,' he asked softly, 'are you losing

your native wit? You're being particularly dim-witted this evening. Perhaps it's the heat.' He sighed. 'Yes, Earl Holland the film star. To me he's just an actor who I hope will do justice to a good part.'

Kate was suddenly overwhelmed by his assurance, his years of experience of people and life. How could he expect her to cope with two film stars staying in the house? And then another thought struck her.

'But, Blake,' she began nervously, 'do they know the kind of marriage . . . I mean, will we have to pretend . . .?'

'The answer to all the questions boggling in your mind is no. They don't know. They're aware we've recently married of course. But it's none of their business what kind of marriage we have. And they've both worked with me before and are fully aware I have no interest in any private life when I'm filming.'

Kate put a hand to her throbbing head. It was all happening too fast. He was just throwing his life at her and expecting her to cope with all his demands. And she couldn't do it.

'What's the matter now?' he barked at her. 'You look like a scared rabbit.'

'It's all very well for you,' she said angrily. 'You've been through this a hundred times. But it's new to me. You chuck bits of information at me and don't give me a chance to understand it.'

'You can't understand it, my girl. It takes a lifetime. And I haven't time to nurse you through it. Once we start shooting all my energy is devoted to my actors and technicians.' He paused to look at her. 'I offered you the job and you accepted . . . were thrilled to accept. I seem to remember,' he drawled, 'that it was the only thing that reconciled you to our marriage. You're planning to be an artist. Well, now's the time to pick up some of the things you'll need to know.'

'That's not fair,' she battled vehemently. 'I'm not planning a film career. I'm going to be a sculptor. And if all this confusion is necessary for film making, I'm glad I won't be part of it.'

'Don't kid yourself, girl, you are part of it. As my wife you have to learn to cope with it and the sooner the better.'

There was a shocked silence as his words sank into Kate's mind.

'Are you mad, Blake?' she demanded. 'You know we're not going to be together long enough for any of that. Six months. That's what you said in London. After that I get my annulment.'

He didn't speak or look at her. Pushing back his chair he got up and lit a cheroot, slowly, maddening her as she waited. Then he moved to the open window and looked out.

'Blake, did you hear me?'

'I could hardly help it the way you're shouting.'

'Well?'

'I'm tired, Kate, too tired to argue about things that aren't relevant at the moment.'

'They may not be relevant to you, but they're my life and my future. Anyway I'm not asking you to argue. I'm telling you. Six months and then I go. If you don't want to pay for my art school, forget it. I'll do without. But whatever you do or say in six months I'll be gone.'

He turned to face her, in his eyes the blank, shuttered look she so hated.

'I warned you I'm tired and don't wish for an argument,' he said coldly, 'but since you seem determined to pursue it, let's look at the facts, shall we? You and I are married. Until I wish it differently we're staying married. You can't get a divorce because I won't give you grounds for one. An annulment without my consent could be very nasty. Personal and private matters have to be brought up in court with doctors and lawyers, and none of that would endear you to your beloved Henri ... if he hasn't in the meantime married his cousin Sophie to whom he was betrothed in childhood.'

He paused and breathed deeply. 'When I'm ready to end our marriage it will be ended, not before.'

'I don't believe this,' Kate whispered, 'even you couldn't be so cruel, so despicable.' She was close to tears. 'You promised it would be temporary ... at the end of the summer I'd get my annulment.' Her voice rose, agitated and frightened. 'I thought we could get through this with our friendship intact. But it's all rigged, isn't it? You planned this all along, and I haven't a chance in hell, have I? What I want or need doesn't mean a row of beans to you because you don't care for anyone.' She was panting now, anger replacing fear. 'Well, one day, Blake Templeton, I'll find out why you really married me, and what you're getting out of this. And then I'll fight you. And you won't find me one of your soft, adoring women. I'll fight and if need be, I'll fight dirty.' Her voice rose and she looked up to see his eyes glittering darkly, a strange electric excitement in the room.

For a moment there was complete silence as she faced him, hands clenched, breast heaving. Then he spoke.

'That's my girl,' he said softly.

'Oh, you . . . .' She whirled and ran out of the room.

Since that day she hadn't seen Blake. He was up early and gone before she was awake. Because their rooms were at opposite ends of the villa, she wasn't even sure if he came home at nights.

And she had never been so alone. After sharing her life with others for so many years, first at boarding school and then in Paris, she felt the loneliness intensely, longing often for someone to talk to, scared when darkness suddenly descended, the only sound the distant lapping of the sea and the faint sighing of the off-shore breeze. Sitting on the terrace alone at night with only her thoughts for company, these had been mainly of Henri.

She had written but heard nothing from him. He was a bad letter writer and she sensed she would have to get through this time without him. What, she wondered, had happened with his grandmother? Had her own absence ruined their chances? Kate knew well enough there could be no marriage without the old lady's consent. And what would her attitude be now that Kate's life had been taken over, however temporarily, by another man?

Whatever the outcome, the old lady wouldn't be persuaded by declarations of love. Eighteen months in Paris had taught Kate that the French rated romantic love very low in the marriage stakes. Money, family and position were the only valid reasons for marriage among the French aristocracy.

And what of Blake's dramatic announcement

about Henri's cousin Sophie? What was her role in Henri's life? And why had Henri never mentioned her? That he didn't love her Kate sensed, strangely confident in their own love for each other. But she wished he would contact her, tell her he loved her and that everything would be all right.

Gradually she allowed her thoughts to return to her father. After the funeral she had pushed all thought of him to the back of her mind, the busy week that followed somehow postponing the moment for grief. But now the anguish of her loss rose to the surface, bringing its own pain.

At first she wept for him, his unhappiness, the last empty years of his life. But then she cried for herself. He had gone, leaving her with her mother who, at their parting in London, had made no pretence of feelings that didn't exist. And Blake. What had her father hoped to gain by forcing her into a marriage she didn't want? For the first time Kate thought of her father dispassionately, seeing a ruthless side of him she had never known. And what was the true reason for Blake's agreement? That he was not the benign, affectionate figure of her childhood she had come to recognise and accept. And certainly since her father's death he had shown a ruthless indifference in his dealings with her, contemptuous of her wishes and feelings.

She sensed he was a complex man, difficult to assess and impossible to manipulate, and she guessed if ever she was to have a say in her own future, she would have to learn to understand him. For the moment she knew only that he was a stranger . . . and a stranger she had married.

A noise intruded into Kate's thoughts. She

could hear voices and laughter, car doors banging. The floodlights came on and she knew Blake was home bringing friends.

In one fluid movement she was out of her chair, sprinting along the terrace and up through the garden to the studio. Inside she closed the door thankfully and stayed in the dark. She would wait till they had gone and then make her way back. Would it be Blanche Dumont and Earl Holland? Or were the guests only for the evening?

As her eyes accustomed themselves to the dark she walked over to the sofa and lay down. Would Blake assume she was in her room asleep or would he come looking for her? She could feel her heart palpitating, and a sudden upsurge of tears swept her as she thought of the future with only the cold protection and financial security of Blake; a life without Henri. Bleakly she wondered how she could bear it.

The moment Kate woke she knew she wasn't alone. She lay quite still, her eyes searching the darkness.

'It's only me.' Blake's voice came quietly out of the dark.

'What is it, Blake? What do you want?'

'I want to know why you're hiding here instead of being down at the villa to welcome our guests.'

'I must have dropped off,' she said lamely.

Blake got up and she flinched back into the cushions as he came towards her.

'Good God, Kate, what is it?'

'Nothing,' she stammered.

He turned away and began to walk up and down, slowly, deliberately, as thought he needed the movement. Then he stood still, his back to her.

'I miss him too, you know,' he said quietly.

Her head went up as her eyes tried to penetrate the dark, to see him clearly.

'Do you?' she whispered.

'It's nothing tangible,' he went on. 'I find myself thinking of things to tell him. And sometimes I turn suddenly as though he was beside me, waiting for me to say something.'

'Oh, Blake.' Kate felt the tears sting her eyes.

'So you see you're not alone in grieving.' He came towards her. 'Don't shut him away. He's still in your feelings and always will be. But it will become less painful.'

'Will it, Blake, truly?'

'Yes, kitten, it will. And don't be ashamed of your tears. Your father was truly worth crying for.'

'Oh, Blake,' she sobbed again, 'I'm so lonely and miserable.'

He stiffened and drew back.

'I've left you alone deliberately these last weeks,' he said, 'to give you a chance to come to terms with things as they are. Life is hard, Kate,' he said harshly, 'and no one can shield you from it.'

She stopped sniffing and sat up, determined to control herself, not to expose herself again to his indifference. He was understanding in some ways, but there was no compassion in him, and he had no affection for her. This was the most important thing she had to face. Blake would never replace her father in her affections.

'All right,' she said dully, 'I'll come in and change.'

'It's too late now. We've had dinner and they've gone to bed. We all have early starts tomorrow. Blanche will be leaving at five for her hair and make-up. Earl and I will be off an hour later.'

'Oh.'

'I came up to tell you I want you with us tomorrow.'

'Oh, no ... I don't think ... I can't ...' she hesitated. Suddenly she couldn't face leaving the security of the villa, facing a group of strangers.

Abruptly Blake moved and switched on the lights. 'What is it with you, Kate? You're fast turning into a mouse. Whatever your faults as a child, you never lacked courage.'

'Maybe that's what marriage to you has done to me,' she said bitterly.

'You told me in London you'd grown up,' he said coldly, 'that I should give you a chance to show it. I've seen no signs of it so far.'

She got up and walked to the basin. Turning on the cold water she splashed it into her face and reached for a towel.

'It would have been better if you'd left me in London. You've twisted my life and you're forcing me to do things I never wanted. What did you expect? Did you think I'd fall into your arms and become your devoted slave, wanting only the life you wish me to lead?'

'Do you realise we can't be in the same room for five minutes without quarrelling?' he demanded. 'Why can't you forget the past? It has to be left behind. Any other woman would revel in the beauty of this place, the holiday you could enjoy, the studio in which you can do the work you love. But all you do is moan.'

'Perhaps you've never been caged and don't understand how it sours everything.' Her voice edged into bitterness. 'If you'd invited me here as your guest, I could have been all the things you want of me. But to marry me against my wishes, and then abandon me to spend my days and nights alone in this villa is unnerving. You shouldn't be surprised I can't cope with it. You're supposed to be such an expert in understanding women,' she finished, her voice low and fierce.

He straightened, his face suddenly stilled. 'It seems I misjudged the situation,' he muttered savagely. In two strides he was at her side, gripping her shoulders. Too late Kate realised he'd misunderstood her.

'No, Blake, I didn't mean . . . please . . .'

He pulled her roughly towards him, his arms round her back, and she felt the anger in his hold as he bent his head and his mouth fastened brutally on hers. Forcing her lips apart he kissed her without tenderness or passion, bruising her lips with his teeth.

She panicked, twisting in his embrace to free herself, but her arms were trapped at her side, her body clamped to his and she couldn't escape. She could feel the thud of his heartbeats, and then his lips suddenly lifted. He murmured something and bent to kiss her again, opening her mouth seductively, his tongue exploring deeply, intimately. Her limbs strangely weak, Kate relaxed against him as the heat rose in her body and her resistance ebbed.

Henri had kissed her many times and expertly, but she had felt nothing like this. She pushed her hands round his back, holding him against her, the feel of his smooth skin under her fingers as she ran her hands up inside his shirt and felt him tremble at her touch. She began to respond to the deepening demand of his kiss and her eyes closed as she gave herself up to the pleasure of his touch.

And then the kiss was suddenly over. He pulled away, leaving her limp and shivering as the warmth of his body left her and reaction set in. She bit her lips hard and looked down at the floor, mesmerised by the pattern of tiles at her feet, shamed at the response he had managed to evoke. She prayed he would say something light and amusing to ease the tension and chase away the depression that threatened to swamp her. But he didn't speak and the silence seemed to stretch unbearably, the only sound their uneven breathing steadying back to normal.

Miserably she knew that any affection or understanding between them had suddenly ended. The Blake Templeton of her childhood was dead, a figment of her imagination.

And then he spoke.

'I'll see you in the morning. Please be ready.'

The next moment she was alone.

CHAPTER FOUR

TONY lifted the megaphone to his lips. 'Lunch everybody. Back at one-fifteen sharp, please.'

Kate gathered her sketch pad and pencils, ramming her hat on to her head and looked across at her husband. He was talking to Archie and they were deep in conversation. She sat back and waited.

She hadn't expected to enjoy coming on location. Introduced to only one or two of the unit, she had been fully aware everyone knew who she was. Determined not to make herself conspicuous, she had found a sheltered spot out of the way, content that first day to watch as the shots were lined up. Everyone waited for the light to be just right, the generator humming, the silver reflectors catching the sun and directing the light where the cameraman wished it to settle. The waiting seemed endless and yet no one became impatient. Blanche Dumont had her own caravan in the shade, and Earl sat in a canvas chair under a tree, quietly reading.

Her knowledge of the script enabled Kate to identify vaguely what was being shot and soon she was absorbed, her eyes constantly returning to her husband. Where others chatted, waiting to be called, Blake's concentration was unremitting. How he sustained the energy in the intense heat she couldn't imagine.

On the second day she had brought her pad and begun to sketch, and from then on she had been accepted. Greeted in the mornings as they arrived, someone always brought her coffee. At lunchtime when the caterer's van opened up and everyone took their food into the shade, Blake came over to collect her. Slowly and steadily they walked up the steep incline away from the beach to the friendly unpretentious Bar-Restaurant at the top where they sat at a scrubbed wooden table, their feet on the cool of the gravel, drinking iced white wine in the shade of a huge plane tree.

Kate chose the same food each day, dipping the thick succulent white asparagus into the spicy vinaigrette sauce, while Blake leaned back, curiously relaxed, watching her eat with lazy amusement, as much at home in the simple café as in one of his sophisticated London restaurants.

The first day she had expected some awkward-ness, but Blake had obviously forgotten the previous night in the studio, and as he had talked, she, too, had lost all self-consciousness. He had explained the morning's work while she had listened, eating slowly, enjoying the light breeze against her face, curiously content.

'What did you think of the scene we just finished?' he asked her, a few days later.

'Mm . . .' She wasn't sure if he really wanted her opinion.

'Well?'

'Their walk along the beach?'

'Yes.'

'I don't know. She seemed a little too eager. It's early on, isn't it? They've just met?'

'That's why it's in long shot. I want the audience to imagine the dialogue from the movement of their heads and bodies as they walk away from camera.'

'Yes, I like that.' She was enthusiastic. 'But Laura ... I think she's still shy of him. She wouldn't arch towards him, She'd wait for him to make the first move. I don't know. It probably sounds a bit silly.'

He didn't answer, looking into the distance, eyes narrowed in concentration.

'Mm ... maybe' he murmured.

When they finished lunch one of the drivers took her home. On the second day she'd asked to stay, but Blake had been firm.

'Don't underestimate the sun. You may have sat in the shade, but you'll probably find your skin's burning when you get under the shower.'

Nodding to her he left, walking briskly back to the beach, her existence forgotten as his mind switched to the afternoon's work.

Now she looked at him. Enormously broad and vital, he wore a white, short-sleeved shirt unbuttoned to reveal the dark hair curling across his chest down to the slim snakeskin belt of his brief black shorts. The small white linen hat with its narrow brim emphasised the black hair, only the smoky grey of the eyes gleaming in the darkly tanned face. The strongly muscled body and straight legs reminded Kate that he swam early each morning, ignoring the pool and swimming strongly round the bay, as fully fit as any member of his crew.

As she watched he turned. Ignoring her completely he strode up the beach and disappeared into the trees. For a moment she was stunned with surprise. Had he forgotten she was there? She felt the red colour creep into her face and wondered what she should do. Before she could move one of the French boys came across the sand towards her.

'I'm to drive you home today,' he volunteered. She smiled briefly and got up. 'Of course,' she murmured. The crew was busy eating, but Earl Holland raised one hand in salute as she left.

The drive home was short. At the top of the hill she looked along the road for Blake, but he wasn't in sight. Nor did she glimpse him as they flashed by the restaurant. Feeling oddly depressed and abandoned she reasoned with herself. He had probably gone to the yacht to watch some 'rushes', the daily quota of film returned from the laboratories. Any number of things could have called him away. And they were not, after all, a normal couple. He owed her no explanation of his movements.

There was no reason therefore for her heart to lurch rather painfully as she walked into the living room that evening to find herself facing only Blanche and Earl. She had dressed with care in a dusty pink sleeveless sheath, telling herself as she put on make-up and perfume, that his movements were of no concern to her. She forced a smile and a greeting.

Earl got up and came towards her, carrying her hand to his lips as he had done that first morning when they met, his eyes lighting up with pleasure as he looked at her, the pale pink of her dress a foil for the tawny chestnut of her hair.

'Beautiful as always,' he murmured and released her hand. She sat down and he poured her an orange juice adding ice and bringing it across.

'I'm hungry,' Blanche announced, 'can't we finish our drinks over dinner?'

'Certainly, if Kate's agreeable,' Earl said quietly, raising his eyebrows at her enquiringly.

'Yes, of course.' Kate was confused. This evening was the first time she had been alone with the two of them. On previous occasions Blake had been there to play host and act as a buffer between her and their high-powered guests.

'You forget, honey,' Blanche drawled looking at Kate, 'we've been up since before dawn and I'm ready for my bed. On call again in the morning.' She shrugged. 'It's fine for you, Earl, you can lie in tomorrow.'

No one commented on Blake's absence, and Kate realised they must assume she knew where he was. The table in the dining room was laid for three, so the servants had obviously been told he would be out for dinner.

As Earl chatted and Blanche quipped back she looked at them both. Blanche was exquisite as always, and no one would guess she had been working in the gruelling heat since early morning. Her jet black hair was held back with a wide band to match the brilliant red of her low-necked, sleeveless dress. The flawless skin and those incredible blue eyes with their long thick lashes emphasised the striking quality of her personality, the almost sultry sexuality that even Kate's inexperienced eye couldn't miss.

Earl Holland was altogether different. She had seen a number of his pictures and he seemed smaller than she'd expected. His hair was thin and reddish, the skin light, his face narrow, the bone structure almost beautiful, giving his head a delicate look with the finely moulded lips and pale blue eyes. More likeable than he appeared in

films, he was less rugged than the camera
suggested. Only his voice was exactly as she
remembered, soft and low, the speech slow and
hesitant. He was ideal casting for the film's hero,
Jason, who falls in love with the eager, intense
Laura, only to find her too draining with her
emotional demands, too exhausting, leading him
in the end to turn to a younger, more superficial
woman.

Kate looked up to see Blanche's eyes on her
enquiringly.

'Sorry,' she said, 'I missed that.'

'Evidently,' Blanche murmured drily. 'I asked,
is it Fiona?' Kate looked blank.

'Is Blake with Fiona?' Blanche asked, her
irritation showing. 'I know she was due in today,
and Blake disappeared like a bat out of hell at
lunchtime. Also he was back late which is not like
the great and noble master.'

'I'm sorry,' Kate said again, 'I don't know.'

'Oh, dear.' Blanche laughed lightly. 'Abandoned already and you don't know who for?'

'That's enough, Blanche,' Earl said firmly.
'And go easy on the wine.'

'Are you hinting I can't handle my liquor,
sweetness, or are you shielding the child bride?
She'll have to learn sometime, won't she?'

'Stop it, Blanche.' Earl's voice was suddenly
hard. 'Go to bed if you can't be civilised.'

'Go to bed and wait for Blake, you mean?'
Blanche demanded archly. 'I fear neither of us
can expect him in our bed now that Fiona's
arrived.'

Kate blushed and looked down at her food, her
appetite deserting her.

'Fiona, my dear innocent, is Blake's latest,'

Blanche went on. 'Which is why she got the part in the film, a part I might add for which she's totally miscast. She was supposed to play Laura of course.' She turned at Kate's start of surprise. 'Didn't you know?' she added maliciously. 'Oh, yes indeed. But, sadly, the money men didn't want her, did they, Earl? Couldn't carry a film, they said. Unknown. Which is exactly what she is . . . unknown,' she emphasised happily. 'The greatest discovery since sliced bread of course in the view of our lord and master. But he couldn't raise a penny on her.'

Blanche lifted her glass and drained it. 'So,' she announced loudly, 'I got the part for which, of course, I'm totally unsuitable. Oh, yes,' she paused dramatically, putting up one hand as though someone was about to argue with her, 'I'm well aware I'm not right for it. But I'm having a lot of fun watching Blake sweat me through it. If I can't entice him to my bed any more, I do at least have his exclusive attention on the set.'

There was a heavy silence as Blanche finished and turned her attention back to her wine glass which she refilled. Miserably Kate wished she knew what to do. Then Earl moved. Walking round the table he took her glass from Blanche and picked her up out of her chair, striding with her from the room, with a muttered, 'Excuse us please, Kate.'

Pushing back her chair Kate wandered through the hall into the living room, sitting down in the dark, a faint light coming into the room from the hall. Carefully she considered what she'd heard. She knew from long ago that Blake's girlfriends were usually the actresses with whom he worked.

Rumour had it he got better performances from
them if he took them to his bed during the
making of the picture. Whether these stories were
true or not, Kate recognised suddenly her
attitude to Blake had changed. Since their kiss
in the studio she had endowed him with some
kind of romantic aura, aware of a tension between
them that was vaguely exciting.

She didn't care about him the way she did
about Henri, of course, but she wasn't indifferent
to him. Perhaps unconsciously she had wanted
him to touch her again, hold her, kiss her. She
flushed in the dark and berated herself for an
idiotic fool, floating in a cloud cuckoo land in
which their brief kiss had been imbued with some
kind of emotional significance. And the truth was
very different. To Blake it had meant nothing, a
moment of anger that sparked off a fleeting
desire, quickly forgotten.

'Please forgive her, Kate.' Earl strolled into the
room just as one of the maids brought coffee and
put the tray on a low table. He sank into an
armchair.

'She's tired and uncertain,' he said gruffly.

'Uncertain?' Kate couldn't hide her surprise.

'She doesn't sound unsure, I know. But she is.
She should never have accepted this part. It's
outside her range and could damage her reputation for slick modern comedy. She took it on as a
sort of challenge, to show Blake she could act
high drama. And he was pretty sure he could
direct her to give the performance he wanted.
And Blanche was right. Once she herself was
contracted to do the picture, he had no problems
raising money.' He put his head back and sighed
heavily. 'But now she's actually doing it, Blanche

is far too professional not to know she's doing it badly. And she's frightened of Fiona coming.'

'Frightened?'

'For one thing Fiona's a marvellous actress. It's true she's had little experience of films, but she has a considerable reputation in the theatre. And Blake was right. She's the perfect Laura. Instead she's playing Louise, the girl Jason goes to in the end.' He ruffled his hair, pushing his hand through it impatiently. 'It's all such a damnable muddle. Everyone seems to be in the wrong part.'

'Except you,' Kate smiled. 'You're ideal for Jason.'

'Thank you.' He grinned boyishly. 'It's a great part.' They sat drinking coffee in companionable silence, neither feeling the need to talk, and Kate relaxed. He was an easy person to be with.

'You don't want to take any notice of Blanche,' he said awkwardly, 'when she gets bitchy. Half the time she doesn't know what she's talking about. And she's only letting off steam ... all that personal stuff about Blake. It's nonsense of course. Blake would have to be out of his mind to prefer anyone else's company when he has you to come home to.'

Kate said nothing.

'I've done three pictures with him, you know,' he went on. 'We're not personal friends exactly, but we know each other pretty well. I like to think he had me in mind when he was writing the Jason part. But no one really knows Blake. I've watched it time and again. He'll let people near him just so far, and then it's curtains. No further. I've often wondered if it's deliberate or just Blake, that he can't help it.'

He lifted his hands behind his head and leaned back, looking at the ceiling. 'Even with girlfriends in the past I've sensed they never got close to him, and it seems right that he didn't marry an actress. With you he can come home to be himself, instead of facing more of the histrionics he has on the set.'

He turned his head to look at her. They could only just see each other in the half dark.

'You don't say much, do you?' He grinned. 'Yet you're the only one who really knows him.'

Kate smiled distantly, but didn't respond with confidences of her own. That would be foolish and possibly dangerous. Blake wouldn't tolerate discussions about his private life between herself and his actors.

'How far does anyone ever know another?' she prevaricated.

'Quite right,' he replied promptly, 'put me in my place. Don't think I'm prying. But it amazes me that Blake managed to find someone like you and persuade you to take him on. I wasn't so lucky,' he said grimly.

'You've been married?' Kate asked.

'You're too young to know, but Blanche and I were married for almost ten years.'

'I'm sorry. I didn't know.'

'It didn't work out. Blanche couldn't cope with the routine of being always with one man. And I was just beginning to make my way. I'm sure I wasn't easy to live with. It's always easy to find reasons for these things in retrospect.'

Kate didn't know what to say. He sounded unhappy.

'You still care for her?' she hazarded.

'There's been no one serious for me since, and

sometimes I've wondered if we could get together again. She might be prepared to settle now. We're both getting older and the parts available to her are changing. Laura might well be the last juvenile lead she'll play.'

He lowered his arms and got up, suddenly restless, standing with his back to her, his eyes on the darkness of the bay where lights were twinkling distantly from several yachts at anchor.

'I'm changing too, slowing down, not doing so many films.' He paused reflectively. 'I think now I'd like a home.' He turned to face her, the moonlight forming a ring of light round his head. 'I've plenty of houses all over the world, waiting for me. But home is different, isn't it? It's coming back to someone you want to see, not just four walls and impeccable cooking.' He laughed shortly. 'I suppose what I'm saying is that I envy Blake.'

He came towards her, looking down into her face in the moonlight. 'And now I must say good night before I make a fool of myself,' he murmured and pulled her out of her chair. Leaning his head down he put his hands to her hair, each side of her head, holding her gently. She didn't move when he lowered his head and she felt his mouth against hers, his lips soft and warm. She closed her eyes and kissed him back lightly.

Suddenly the room was flooded with light. Kate jerked her head back, but Earl didn't move, holding her firmly, taking his mouth away from hers slowly before he straightened up.

'What the hell's going on here?' It was Blake. His voice was coldly furious, and Kate pulled herself up defensively. Before she could move Earl spoke.

'I was just saying good night to your wife,' he said softly, stressing the word 'wife', 'and now I must go to bed.'

He bowed to Kate and moved towards Blake to pass him. But Blake stood blocking the exit.

'I think I'm entitled to an explanation,' he said angrily.

Earl stopped. 'I hope you're not about to lose your cool, Blake. I was kissing your wife to thank her for listening to my troubles. And now I'd like to go upstairs.'

Earl's voice was mild, without a trace of humour or emotion. For a moment the two men looked hard at each other. Almost of equal height, Earl seemed somehow fragile when compared with the rugged strength that always emanated from Blake. Kate longed to run away, but kept quite still, guessing it could precipitate anger between the two men.

At last Blake moved and Earl walked past him.

'Good night,' he said quietly, and Kate listened to his footsteps up the stairs.

'I think I'll be off to bed, too.' She moved nervously to edge past Blake.

'Just a minute.' She stopped. 'What exactly has been going on here?' he demanded tightly.

'Nothing,' Kate replied calmly, determined not to lose her temper. 'The three of us had dinner and Blanche wasn't feeling too well so she went to bed. Earl and I sat and talked.'

'In the dark?'

'For heavens sake, Blake,' she was fast losing patience with him. 'You don't have to upset yourself. I wouldn't talk to Earl about our marriage.'

When he didn't comment she looked up into

his face. He was deathly tired, dark rings round his eyes, the skin almost grey with fatigue.

'Are you planning to have an affair with him?' he asked jerkily.

'Of course not,' she said shortly. 'I don't go round having affairs with people.'

'It's never too late to start,' he said harshly.

'Stop it, Blake. There's no reason for you to bait me. You know I'm in love with Henri. Why should I be interested in other men?'

He turned his head and they looked at each other without speaking. She wondered if he was thinking of the evening in the studio when he had kissed her and she had responded to him. His eyes were half-closed, intent on her face, but she couldn't tell if he was still angry.

Suddenly she took the initiative.

'You look awful,' she said rudely.

He laughed shortly. 'I'm starving. Do you think you could find me something to eat? I haven't had dinner.'

'Did you ask them to leave you something?'

'No.'

'They've gone now.'

'Mm . . .' he murmured.

'Oh, all right' she said crossly. 'I'll make you something. But you'll have to come down and eat in the kitchen. I'm not climbing up here to serve you.'

'Eat in the kitchen?' His voice rose in astonishment.

'People do it, you know, all over the world . . . eat in their own kitchens.'

His face creased into a real smile and involuntarily she smiled back.

'Right,' he said, 'lead the way. Show me my kitchen.'

'You're impossible, do you know that?'

'Of course,' he grinned, not at all abashed.

In the kitchen Kate opened the fridge. Ham, grilled with an omelette, she decided, and mushrooms. Deftly she began preparations.

'Do you want help?' he asked politely.

'You can cut some ham,' she replied coolly. 'Knives in that drawer,' and she pointed.

'Yes, ma'am' he saluted smartly and went to work.

'And start the coffee,' she added.

'This is all very cosy, isn't it?' he asked. 'Almost as though we were married.'

'If you want this meal I suggest you give up childish banter,' Kate commented, her voice suspiciously quiet.

Fifteen minutes later she dished up the ham and omelette, fluffy and oozing with mushrooms. Sitting down opposite him she helped herself to coffee.

'Wow,' he said tucking in hungrily, 'you can cook.'

'Certainly,' she said tartly, 'what do you think I did with my time in Paris?'

He looked up, his mouth full, his eyes alight with amusement.

'I could tell you, but I don't think I'd better.' She stuck out her tongue at him and then watched him eat. Gradually the colour came back into his face, and she wondered where he'd been. Surely if he'd spent the evening with Fiona she would have fed him? Or maybe their emotions got the better of them and food wasn't on their minds. Kate felt the colour rise in her face as she pictured Blake in the grip of emotion with a woman, losing control and revealing his true feelings. She wondered what it would be like to share such moments with him.

Looking up she found his eyes on her, mocking, questioning, and hurriedly lifted her cup to her lips, striving to turn her thoughts away from the man who was her husband.

'Well, now,' he drawled, 'I wonder what wicked thoughts gave rise to such an overwhelming blush?' He leaned back and lit a cheroot, the smoke curling round his face.

Kate looked down into her cup.

'Don't worry, kitten, I'm not going to pry into your feelings. I know they aren't my concern.' He stood up. 'And now I must go and do some work, so I'll leave you.'

'Work? Now?' Kate was aghast. 'But you're desperately tired!'

He looked down at her, mockery clear in his face.

'How wifely,' he murmured. 'I wonder what further wifely delights could be mine if I had the time to find out?'

'Your arrogance knows no bounds, does it?' she demanded angrily.

'I fear that's probably true. Good night, little one, and thank you for my meal. I enjoyed it. All of it' he stressed.

Fiona turned out to be quite unlike Kate's expectations. Watching her work the next morning Kate was amazed at the slim, slight figure with its halo of thick curls that stood out from her rather small head, the face pale and insignificant.

When lunch was called Kate expected to be collected by her driver and was surprised to see both Fiona and Blake heading across the sand towards her. Introductions were made and they walked up the beach. Fiona was in khaki shorts and tee-shirt, an old poncho hat on the riotous blonde hair. They sat at their usual table, and Fiona spent the whole time toying with her melon. She conversed easily, and she and Blake talked shop about film and theatre people whose names meant nothing to Kate.

As she watched, Kate realised it would be easy to underestimate the young actress. When animated, her face was mobile and sensitive, rather compulsive to watch, and Kate wondered if the camera eye would pick that up.

'You sculpt?' she asked Kate.

'I'm learning,' Kate corrected.

'Where?'

'I'm hoping to go to art school in the autumn,' she answered looking defiantly at Blake. But he was busy with his food and didn't glance up.

'May I come and see your studio while I'm here?' she asked next. 'Blake's told me how lovely it is.'

'Of course.' Kate found herself being stiff with the other woman, wondering at Blake. How could he have an affair with a woman like Blanche, with her vibrant, extrovert personality, and then pick this tense, pale, thin girl with apparently little in the way of looks to recommend her?

'When?' Fiona asked.

'Whenever you have the time,' Kate replied looking again at Blake.

'Great,' Fiona enthused. 'And you will come and see our villa, won't you? It's just lovely. Blake picked it out for us and we're really enjoying the peace and privacy.'

Kate marvelled at the other woman's nerve in talking to Blake's wife so openly about her relationship with him. Then it occurred to her that Fiona might well know the truth about Blake's marriage.

'Will you bring her one evening?' Fiona asked Blake.

'If there's time,' he answered absently, 'but she has a lot of work. Don't forget Kate's here also to do a job.'

Fiona took this quite philosophically. 'Whatever you say, Blake,' she said amiably.

Kate found she couldn't eat and picked up her wine glass. She was beginning to recognise that the sophistication of Blake's emotional life was way beyond her. And she felt pity for the girl at her side. If she loved Blake she was in for a lot of heart-ache because he wouldn't stay with her. And Kate suddenly realised why Blake changed his girlfriends with his films. It was the film that was important. Nothing else really mattered beside his work. Probably all his emotions went into that, with little left for the woman of the moment. And if he couldn't involve himself deeply with a woman, then of course he'd become bored with the same face, the same body.

She felt slightly sick with revulsion at the life he led, they all led, and she longed suddenly for Henri and the simple, safe life he offered. Once she was married to him, she'd be free of Blake.

Dear God. What hope was there of marriage to the man she loved, when she was tied to Blake who neither cared for her nor . . .

'Will you excuse me, please?' she murmured and got up. She had to get away. 'I think I'll get back.'

Both looked up from their conversation and Blake got to his feet.

'What's the matter?' he asked sharply.

'Nothing. Perhaps the heat . . .' She was now desperate to get away from him. As he came round the table towards her, she turned and fled up the steps to the road. Wildly she looked for the car, but there was nothing, nobody.

'What the hell are you playing at?' Blake demanded as he caught up with her. 'You left your hat.'

He took her arm and put the hat on her head, but she pulled away from him sharply, shaking off the touch of his hand. Roughly he clamped his hands to her shoulders, turning her round to face him. Seeing the distress in her face he pulled her away from the restaurant towards a clump of trees by the side of the road. As they reached the shade he let her go.

'What is all this?' he demanded.

'Nothing'. She began to shiver. 'I just . . . I don't want to . . .'

'Kate?' His hand touched her hair, brushing it away from her face.

'Don't touch me,' she shouted. 'I can't bear you to touch me. Leave me alone. Go away. Just send the car for me and let me go back.'

He flinched away from her and she looked up to see his mouth set.

'You're hysterical,' he said tautly.

'Probably,' she said miserably. 'I can't stand it any more. I wish I'd never come here. I hate being married to you. I want to go home.'

By this time she was shivering uncontrollably, the sweat coming out on her face, her body cold and damp.

With an impatient exclamation Blake bent and picked her up, carrying her along the road till they reached the sandy path that led to the beach.

'André,' he called loudly, 'André.'

Someone came running and Blake barked orders. But Kate was aware of little as she hid her face in his chest, her hands clinging to him as he carried her to the car.

The journey seemed endless and she made one attempt to talk to him.

'The film,' she whispered, 'you must go back.'

'To hell with the film,' he said calmly as he held her on his lap, a blanket round her. 'Hold on, we're nearly home.'

Her eyes were beginning to burn and her head ached. She didn't have the strength to talk, so she sobbed lightly into his chest, her lips against the soft curly hair, in her ears the sound of his heart beating.

CHAPTER FIVE

THE next forty-eight hours passed in a haze of pain and discomfort. Kate was either too hot or shivering with cold, dimly aware of constant changes of bed linen, her face and hands bathed at intervals, the sound of her own voice crying and moaning.

The first time she woke fully conscious, it was night.

'I'm thirsty,' she declared loudly, and someone came. She thought for a moment it was Blake, but of course it couldn't be in the middle of the night. He would be with Fiona or asleep in his own wing, or working downstairs in his study. She drank eagerly and slept again.

The next time she woke her head was clear and she could focus on the room around her. Someone lifted her against banked pillows and put a table with food across her knees. Scrambled eggs, toast and tea. She tried to lift her hand and found the effort too great. Looking up she recognised Annabelle and smiled wanly.

The older woman sat on the side of the bed and fed her, chatting quietly in French, smiling gently. Kate didn't follow everything she said, but found the words comforting. Halfway through the meal she slipped down in the bed and fell instantly asleep once more.

It was dark again when she finally woke feeling much stronger. Swinging her legs out of bed she tried to stand to get to the bathroom. Staggering unevenly she made it to the end of the bed where she collapsed on to the rug, her head dizzy.

The door opened and Blake stood there. She looked up at him in astonishment. He was in a dressing gown, the thick black towelling belted round the waist and ending at the knees.

'Are you all right?' He bent to lift her on to the bed while she tried to figure out what he was doing in her room in the middle of the night. But her brain couldn't seem to put the thoughts together.

'Were you making for the bathroom?'

'Yes.' She nodded vigorously.

'Come on,' he said quietly, 'let's try again.'

Leaning heavily against him she made it and released herself from his hold, closing the bathroom door firmly against him. The wash refreshed her and she went back to the bedroom hoping he'd gone. He was standing by the shutters and came immediately to help her into bed. She lay back exhausted as Blake tiptoed to the door.

'Blake?'

He came and stood to look down at her.

'What happened?' she asked weakly.

'You've been ill. Heat stroke. You've had it rather badly and we've all been worried. But you're over it now. A couple more days and you'll be up and about.'

'But . . .' she swallowed heavily, 'the sculpting . . . Earl. I should have been working with him . . .'

'There's no panic for any of that,' Blake said quietly, 'we've re-scheduled Earl so that his free mornings will be next week, and he's looking forward to that.'

'I'm sorry,' she whispered, 'it must have caused a lot of trouble.'

'Yes,' he said, smiling down at her, 'you're a terrible patient, do you know that?'

'Was I?' She smiled weakly. 'Have you been cross?'

'Me . . . cross? With my angelic nature?' He grinned.

'Oh, go away. You're impossible.'

'That's what you said the last time we talked, so I'd better go and let you sleep.'

'Mm . . .' she agreed sleepily.

After that Kate made rapid progress. She spent a couple of days dragging herself round the villa, but within a week she was back in the studio. The mornings were spent with Earl. There were several portraits to finish, some of which had been roughed out. And there was the final one that Laura destroys at the end of the story. A consummately experienced actor, Earl was totally relaxed, an ideal model.

They worked with intense concentration for a couple of hours at a stretch, and then made a break, going for a swim, sitting in the grass outside or just chatting in the studio. It was on the third morning Kate asked how the film was progressing.

'It's picking up and it looks as though Blake will finish on schedule.'

'Was he behind schedule?'

'Mike Bolton, the editor, did his best while Blake was away, doing odd inserts, but Blake insisted no work was done with any of us till he got back.'

'Got back? Has he been away?'

'Away from the unit, I mean.'

'Oh.'

'You look mystified, love,' he said lightly, 'don't you know he never stirred from your room while you were ill?'

'No.' Kate was shocked. 'I didn't realise . . .'

'Wouldn't you have done the same for him?' Earl quizzed her with his eyes.

'Of course' she replied unthinkingly, 'but I don't have a picture to finish.'

'Once you were on the mend he went to sleep for about fifteen hours, and now he's working like a fiend to catch up the time lost.'

'Oh.'

'When Dr Anderson came from London he offered to bring a nurse, but by then you were over the worst and Blake didn't think it necessary.'

'Dr Anderson?' Kate asked faintly, beginning to realise she had missed quite a lot of what had happened.

'Blake insisted on a second opinion. The local doctor obviously knew what he was doing, but Blake was concerned about possible complications.'

'I see.'

'He was very worried about you, naturally. I've never seen him so concerned. You weren't at all good, you know, for a few days.'

Kate wondered if it had been Blake who had changed her when she was soaked in perspiration, and the colour rose to her face as she realised nursing her would have involved him in physical intimacies of which she knew nothing.

She looked up to see Earl's eyes on her with some curiosity, and pulled herself together. This was not the moment to agitate over what had happened. There was work to do.

'Shall we get on?' she asked brightly.

It was a week later and Kate was alone. She had
lost weight and tired easily, going to bed each
afternoon and sleeping heavily only to get up to a
solitary meal before returning to bed. Very rarely
did anyone come back for dinner, and she was in
bed by the time Earl and Blanche returned, their
voices briefly audible before the house settled for
the night. She hadn't seen Blake and assumed he
was now back with Fiona.

A knock on the door interrupted her thoughts.
She called out and Louis appeared in the
doorway.

'You have a visitor,' he announced.

'Thank you,' she smiled, 'I'll be right down.'

She looked at herself in the mirror. Should she
change? The pale blue sundress with its crisp
halter neck was a little informal for a stranger.
Perhaps it was Fiona coming as promised.

Walking down the stairs she saw a man in the
open living room, his back to her. Not Fiona
then, she thought, and in that moment he turned.

'Henri.'

She let go of the banisters and flew down the
stairs straight into his arms.

'Katherine.'

Held close to his familiar figure she clung to
him convulsively.

'Oh, Henri ... it's so wonderful to see you.
Why didn't you let me know you were coming?'

She looked at him eagerly, lifting her face for
his kiss. He was looking down at her, frowning
heavily.

'What is this?' he demanded. 'You look terrible
... so thin and pale. What is the matter?'

'I've been ill, but it was nothing. It's all over,' she said dismissively.

'*Diable*,' he muttered furiously, 'how is it that you are away from me for a matter of weeks and allowed to become ill?' His face hardened as he looked round the room. 'This house . . . it is the home of . . .'

She nodded.

'I cannot talk to you here. We go,' he said seriously. 'You will come with me to my hotel to take tea?'

'Oh, yes,' she smiled happily.

'*Bon*. You will inform the servants you are with me.'

'Yes, Henri,' she said meekly.

Louis must have been hovering because he was in the hall as they walked through.

'Louis, Monsieur du Bois is taking me out to tea,' she said. 'I'll be back for dinner.'

'*Peut-être*,' Henri said clearly.

Arrived at the Carlton in Cannes, Henri ignored the famous terrace overlooking the Croisette, and marched her purposefully through the marble columns of the foyer into one of the lounges where they sank into deep armchairs and he ordered iced tea.

'Now we must talk,' he said gravely.

'Yes,' she agreed nervously. Now that her first pleasure at his appearance was settling, she wondered why he had come.

'First,' he began a shade pompously, 'I must tell you this whole thing has been a great shock to me, and to grandmère. I have told her nothing about this man . . . Templeton. She knows only that your father died and you cannot visit. This she understands. It is family.' He paused. 'And now, *chèrie*, I would like some explanation of what has happened.'

Kate felt unexpectedly tongue-tied. She bit her lips and wished they were somewhere else. It was difficult in this public place with people drifting in and out, and waiters looking at them from open doorways.

'Well,' she began, 'did you get my letters?'

'Yes, yes, of course. But I am not good at letters. You know that.'

'But you didn't write at all, Henri,' she complained. He looked somewhat shamefaced and patted her knee lightly, like an uncle reassuring a small niece, Kate thought suddenly. She looked at him properly for the first time. He was just the same. Slim, blond, exquisitely dressed in silk with formal shirt and tie. Yet she found her heart didn't melt in quite the same way as it had always done in Paris. His face was set frowningly and he was looking solemn and displeased.

'Well?' he demanded.

'Henri, please, I'm nervous. I've a lot ... I mean a lot has happened to me.'

'That is what I am here to find out,' he said rather coldly.

'But why are you so severe? You frighten me,' she murmured.

At that he turned and smiled, his face softening, his eyes on her mouth.

'You don't understand,' he said huskily, 'I love you and want to marry you. You tell me you love me, but suddenly you are married to someone else, a friend of your father's.' His voice was low and vehement. 'What do you expect me to feel?'

He looked away from her. 'Are you still a virgin?' he demanded bluntly.

Kate blushed as he turned to her, his eyes cold and hard. She evaded his gaze and stared down at her hands. 'Yes, of course,' she said, 'it's nothing like that.'

'I believe you,' he said after a moment's hesitation.

'I should hope so,' she said on a spurt of anger.

'Very well. Now tell me.'

'My father . . . when he died, in his will . . . we, my mother and I, we found there was no money.'

'No money?' Henri repeated in astonishment.

'My mother had been spending rather freely and it had all gone. The house and the . . . art collection were all mortgaged.'

'*Mon Dieu*,' Henri said forcefully.

'Blake Templeton had been . . . financing my father and . . . us in the last years.'

'Because he wished to marry you?'

'Oh, no,' Kate said firmly. 'He didn't want to marry me. My father demanded it of him.'

Henri turned fully to look at her, his face red, his eyes angry. 'I am not a child, Katherine, nor an idiot. Why else would he waste his time financing an old man?'

'You don't understand. Blake's been my father's friend for years. When my father was . . . very ill . . . dying, he wanted me protected because I'm a minor.' Kate's voice died away as she realised her explanation was feeble and lacked conviction.

'My patience is running out, Katherine. It is bad enough all that you tell me, but it is no reason for a marriage between you and this old man.'

Kate giggled to hear Blake described as an old man. 'He's not exactly old.'

'So much the worse,' Henri went on coldly. 'Kindly tell me why he had to marry you? Why couldn't your father have left you in his guardianship till your majority?'

Kate nibbled her lips. Since this was exactly what she had asked herself so often, she found it difficult to answer.

'I don't know,' she said eventually, hanging her head.

'*Précisément*.' He paused, his brow still knitted in anger, and Kate felt nervousness threaten her happiness. He had never been angry with her before.

'So what did your mother say to all this? Why are you not with her? She is your guardian now your father is dead.'

'My mother doesn't want me to live with her,' Kate replied bluntly. 'She has her own life to lead.' This scene wasn't going at all as she'd planned. She turned to him impulsively. 'But what does it matter? I'm almost eighteen and then I'll get an annulment. Blake can't force me to stay with him once I'm of age.'

'What puzzles me is that he couldn't force you to marry him whatever your age. So you must have agreed. More than that, you must have had your mother's permission. I don't understand any of this, Katherine, and what I hear I don't like. It is not fitting in the woman who is to be my bride, and the mother of my children.'

'Henri this is silly,' she was coaxing him, 'you know I love only you, and nothing's really changed. If you love me we'll still be married. It'll just have to be postponed for a while.'

'I don't know. If you are to be believed, this man who has paid much to marry you has not

consummated the marriage. I ask myself why?
Perhaps he is waiting, courting you, planning to
win your love.'

'Oh, no, Henri, it's not like that. He's not
interested in me. He has loads of girlfriends. I'm
just a duty he feels he owes to my father.' She
paused wondering if she should tell him what she
herself suspected. 'I think my father was worried
that you and I would marry.'

Henri's head shot up and he looked at her,
pride and anger in his face.

'Not because it was you,' she added hastily, 'but
because he thought . . . I mean, he asked Blake to
marry me so that I wouldn't run away with you. He
didn't know we were planning to wait.'

Henri's expression didn't soften. Instead he
looked intently down at the floor as the waiter
appeared with their tea, served it and left them.
Looking at him Kate's uneasiness rose.

'What you say may be right,' he said rather
heavily, 'but it still doesn't explain why this man
married you. You could refuse an annulment and
stay with him for his money.'

Kate laughed. 'But I wouldn't dream of it. I
don't like him. He's successful certainly, and
powerful, but he's ruthless and unkind. He has
no fondness for me. Anyway, I hardly ever see
him. He's in the middle of a film at the moment
and works from morning to night. Also there are
other people staying with us, the stars of the
film.'

'Actors.' Henri's voice was contemptuous.

Kate ignored the gibe. 'And I'm working on the
film myself,' she added proudly.

'Working? Is that how you became ill? Does he
make you work for him?'

'No, of course not.' Kate was shocked. 'It's work I love. I'm doing some sculpting. You see the main character is . . .'

'Spare me,' he interrupted, 'I'm not interested in all that. It is of no importance to me . . . to us.'

Kate laughed lightly, although she was hurt at his cutting tone. 'Except that I'll be going to art school when I leave here.'

'Naturally all that will stop when we marry,' he commented frostily.

'Oh, no, Henri, I can't stop sculpting. I have to learn properly. But it doesn't have to be London. I can study in Paris after we're married.'

'You are mistaken, Kate, if you think I will permit my wife to become a student at an art college where all kinds of undesirables abound. When we are married naturally we will live at the chateau with grandmere, and you will be too busy having babies to sculpt.'

For the first time since their meeting there was an uneasy silence between them. He only called her Kate when he was seriously displeased with her, she thought irrelevantly. No sculpting. Living with his formidable grandmother who didn't want her, but wished him to marry his cousin Sophie.

'And will Sophie be living with us also?' she asked spitefully.

He swung round to face her, his eyes livid with anger, his mouth tight with disapproval. 'What do you know about Sophie?' he demanded tautly.

Kate sighed, regretting her outburst. 'Blake told me she's your cousin and you were betrothed as babies.'

'And may I ask how your husband found out about all this?'

She blushed. 'It seems he was having me

watched in Paris and he found out all about . . .
your family,' she ended miserably.

'*Diable*,' he muttered. 'He sounds a most
likeable character, this husband of yours. And
now I think I cut his throat.'

Kate had forgotten how dramatically Henri
could express himself, and she stifled an
involuntary giggle at the thought of Henri trying
to cut Blake's throat. Blake would be more than a
match for the younger man. The conversation
was becoming slightly unreal, like some theatrical
tragedy, but she was determined to placate
Henri's feelings.

'Won't you tell me about Sophie?' she coaxed
him. 'Would I like her?' She put her hand
affectionately on his arm and looked anxiously up
into his face. He leaned forward and put his hand
over hers, his fingers tightening rather painfully
on her wrist.

'That is the other reason why I came,' he said
seriously, 'to tell you about her.'

Kate's throat contracted and she felt a piercing
premonition of pain and rejection. For a moment
she closed her eyes, trying to shake it off.

'It is true,' Henri was saying, 'Sophie and I
were betrothed. It was a hope our mothers shared
when we were little. But both our father were
against it. Sophie's father is still alive and doesn't
wish for the marriage between us. And naturally
Sophie obeys him in everything. When I went
down this time I decided to tell her about you.'
His face lit up with sudden affection. 'And do
you know what she said? She wished me all
possible happiness.'

'That was nice of her,' Kate commented
thankfully.

'She was wonderful,' he went on, 'quite light-hearted, insisting I must feel no guilt.'

'Why should you feel guilty?'

'She loves me,' he said simply. 'She has always loved me. If I asked her, she would defy her father and marry me. And that would be the greatest sacrifice she could make.'

'Oh.'

'You see, she is not beautiful like you. She is small and a little plain. So it will not be easy for her to love again and be accepted for herself. Her father is very rich and will marry her to someone who wishes for her money.'

'Oh, dear.' Kate was beginning to feel quite sorry for the absent Sophie.

'So I came to tell you grandmère insists we wait. Sophie must accustom herself to losing me and then grandmère will agree to your visit, next year perhaps.'

'Next year?' Kate was horrified. 'But what happens in between?'

'We will meet occasionally. It will be a test for us also. Sophie and I agreed this was the best way to look at it. She is of course very sorry that she causes the postponement, and she has even offered to see grandmère and persuade her to let you come sooner. But that of course I couldn't permit. And naturally Sophie would do nothing to displease me.'

Kate's mind was beginning to reel with confusion. From the poor little rich girl, Sophie was changing into a very smart young lady who knew Henri very well indeed and had by no means bowed out of the running. And the way Henri talked about her was disconcerting. His voice softened with affection, his eyes warmed at the thought of her.

Her head was aching and she wished herself out of this. Meeting him again hadn't turned out the way she'd imagined, and she was disturbed by a feeling of uncertainty. Perhaps she'd changed. Or possibly she hadn't seen enough of him in Paris to understand what he was really like and what marriage meant to him. He seemed shocked at her family's loss of fortune. In fact he'd been shocked at everything she'd told him.

'I'd like to go home now, Henri,' she said rather faintly.

Instantly he was all concern and affection. 'You must rest,' he said firmly. 'I will arrange a room for you, and later we will go out to dinner and I will kiss you in the moonlight,' he finished ardently, and Kate felt she must have imagined his coldness. Weakly she agreed, and went upstairs to sleep deeply in the rather opulent, impersonal hotel bedroom the housekeeper unlocked for her.

They ate in a quiet corner of the formally elegant Carlton Grill, discreetly hidden from the ravishing gowns and sleek dinner jackets of other diners. As the light began to dim outside and the crystal chandeliers came to life, Kate wondered miserably why she wasn't deliriously happy to be with Henri in such romantic surroundings. Watching the deft hands of the waiter pouring cream and cognac into her Steak Diane, she felt lost and oddly remote, almost a stranger, acting out a part in an alien drama.

After their meal he took her for a walk along the beach and kissed her in the dark, passionately and long, until she became aware he was more roused than she'd ever known him to be.

'I must have you, *petite*,' he breathed. 'I don't

want to wait till marriage. Will you come to me in Paris . . . soon?'

She stood still in his embrace, strangely shocked. He had changed, she decided definitely. Perhaps it was the heat or the moonlight. But she sensed it was more than that. She'd felt his fingers on her body, his hands moving expertly over her dress. He would never have caressed her so intimately in Paris.

Did he think she was now fair game, married to another man? Did that change her in his eyes? None of it was clear. She knew only she had sudden misgivings about him. And she wasn't responding as ardently as she had done in the past. Under her closed lids an image returned vividly of the last time she'd been kissed. When Blake had touched her she'd melted, her skin tingling, her body longing for closer intimacy. She'd responded to him as she never had with Henri.

Sensing her withdrawal, he turned her in his arms and they walked back to the car without speaking. At the villa he switched off the engine.

'Eh, *alors, chèrie*,' he said lightly, 'it is time to say good night. I leave early in the morning and we will not meet again before I go.'

She said nothing, in the grip of a strange certainty that they would not see each other again. She felt a tight constriction in her throat as desolation swept over her. It couldn't be the end, she thought unhappily. Something had gone wrong between them, but they'd sort it out. They loved each other.

'Henri . . .' she began.

'Hush, *chérie*.' He put a finger across her lips. Then he got out of the car and opened her door, helping her out. His arms went round her and his mouth seized hers, fiercely passionate and demanding. She stood still, willing herself to respond, but nothing happened. She seemed to be with a stranger.

At last he let her go. The headlights blazed briefly as she stood dazed, and then he was gone.

CHAPTER SIX

UNSTEADILY she made her way down to the house wondering what time it was. The villa was dark, and she hoped fervently she wasn't locked out. Reaching for the handle relief flooded through her as the front door opened, and she let herself into the dark, thankful for the first time that the servants slept out. Blanche and Earl would be long in bed and Blake . . .

The study door opened suddenly and she swung round in the dark.

'Just a moment.' It was Blake. 'I'd like a word with you.'

She stood still, her heart hammering with shock. 'I'm tired, Blake, it'll have to wait till morning.'

'Now, Kate. Please don't put me to the trouble of fetching you,' he said coldly.

She walked towards the stairs. 'There's no need to be childish. I'm simply not in the mood for talking.'

'Ane I'm not in the mood for arguing,' he said striding towards her.

'All right.' They both stopped, and she walked past him into the study. The room was in darkness, but for a table lamp directing a beam of light on to his desk strewn with papers and drawings. The windows were open, the shutters closed.

Kate stood inside the door as Blake crossed to his desk and sat down behind it facing her.

Looking at him she remembered she hadn't seen him since her illness, and with a pang she realised she hadn't yet thanked him for nursing her. Embarrassed she looked down and bit her lip, trying to keep a tight control on her emotions. The evening with Henri had upset her more than she cared to admit, and she was afraid if Blake lectured her she would lose what little composure she had left.

'Please sit down, Kate.'

'No, Blake, I'm not going to be here long enough.' Her voice sounded childish.

'As you wish. So will you tell me where you've been?' he asked quietly.

She looked up, reassured by his tone. 'I left a message,' she explained carefully.

'Louis told me you'd gone out with a gentleman to have tea.'

'That's right.'

'So, where were you and with whom?'

'I've spent the afternoon and evening with Henri.'

'So why have you come back? Why didn't you run off with him?' he asked tautly.

'Is that what you want to know?' Her voice shook, distress clear in her face. 'Well, it's none of your business. What I think, what I feel or plan has nothing to do with you. My feelings were of no interest to you when we got married. Why are you concerned now? Or is it that you want to know what we did together, how we spent our time?'

She was panting now, her precious control slipping. 'Well you can let your imagination run riot. We found somewhere to be alone and make love . . . ardent passionate love. Does that satisfy

your curiosity?' She stopped. She knew if she
didn't get out of there she would start to cry, and
nothing would allow her to break down in front
of him. She put her head back against the door,
tears glistening on her lashes.

Blake sat silent and motionless, his face blurred
as she looked at him through her tears. When he
didn't speak she turned rather blindly to open the
door behind her.

In an instant he was across the room at her
side. Taking hold of her shoulders he turned her
round and lifted her face with one hand, looking
down into her wet eyes.

'So now you know what it's all about, do you?'
he asked softly. 'I wonder. If that's so, I've
misjudged your Henri.'

He reached a hand to her hair and pulled her
head towards him, bending slowly till he touched
his lips to hers. His mouth was cool and dry, the
pressure gentle and persuasive.

Kate stood indifferent in his hold, too
exhausted to protest or pull away, tears of
weariness and depression spilling down her
cheeks to his lips. At the touch of her tears his
hold tightened cruelly and he pulled her hard
against him, his arms closing round her, his kiss
deepening as he opened her lips wide to exact
punishment.

She felt the heat rise in his body, and a quiver
of response trembled through her, shocking her
into awareness. Her mouth moved under his and
she leaned towards him, a yielding lethargy in her
body.

At her response his hand moved down her
back, fingers caressing her spine while his lips
began a slow sensual caress over hers. Kate

shivered. The cold numb indifference she had experienced with Henri only minutes earlier flamed into life at Blake's touch. She urged her body closer, lifting her breasts against him and raising her hands to his head, fingers threading through the crisp thick hair.

Eyes closed she was dimly aware he had carried her over to the sofa, where he put her down and lay on top of her, his hard body embedding itself into hers. Shuddering with excitement, her mouth opened to his and she kissed him back compulsively, passionately. Her hands moved to his shoulders, fingers feeling for the smooth skin through the silk of his shirt, her body arching against the heavy weight of muscled hips and thighs.

Lying back, eyes closed, sensations rushed through her as his lips left hers to move down her throat searching for the roundness of her breasts. She felt his breath hot against her skin as he bent his lips to her nipples and buried his face in the softness of her skin.

She cried out as a flare of desire raced through her and shook her into sudden panic. Pulling her arms from his shoulders, she pushed her fists into his chest, her breath coming in short gasps. He wasn't expecting it and drew back instinctively as she dragged her legs from under him and was clear of the sofa in a flash of movement. But he was too quick for her. Before she could open the door he had her pinned against it, his hands either side of her, imprisoning her, barring her escape.

Her body trembling uncontrollably, her mouth dry with fear, Kate stared at him, mesmerised by the stormy darkness of his eyes and the mouth released from its firm control, revealing the full sensuality of the lips. She had always sensed she wouldn't be able to cope if Blake was ever roused to anger. But this was far worse than anything she could have imagined. He had released some wildness in her, some emotion she didn't understand and couldn't control. She had wanted him to go on touching her, exciting her and bringing her to some kind of surrender to his demands and her own desires.

But how was it possible for him to take her to such heights of passion, rousing needs and longings she had never dreamed she could feel? Was she going mad? This was Blake, not Henri. Her thoughts whirled incoherently as she continued to gaze at him, confusion in her shadowed eyes, the tear-drenched cheeks pale with shock.

And then he spoke, his breathing even, his voice harsh.

'So you've been making love with your Henri, have you?' he taunted, reminding her how this had started. 'Do you take me for a fool, a raw inexperienced boy who can't recognise outraged virginity?' He smiled mockingly, his head bent to her face, his breath against her mouth. 'So,' he murmured, his voice low and caressing, 'what did happen tonight? Did your Henri try it on? And this avalanche of emotion that erupts every time I touch you . . . does he enjoy that too?'

The crack sounded loud in the quiet room as her hand connected with his cheek. He didn't flinch or move away.

'I thought not.' His voice was now faintly amused. 'You've a long way to go, kitten.'

'You monster,' she breathed furiously, 'I hate you, Blake Templeton. I've never hated anyone the way I loathe you,' she stormed at him eyes flashing.

'I know.' He smiled, mocking her, his voice infuriatingly calm. 'I can feel it when I hold you in my arms, trembling with excitement.'

She lifted her hand again, but this time he caught it, hard fingers round her wrist. 'Not again I think,' he said coldly, and Kate watched his eyes harden, the smile leave his face. He released her and turned away.

'Perhaps there's something we should get straight,' he said calmly, sitting again at his desk. 'When I want a female body I don't have to resort to virgins. As for you,' he looked across at her, his face inscrutable, 'you're just beginning to discover your own sexuality . . . experimenting. And that's perfectly normal at your age, all part of growing up. I don't flatter myself it's anything personal. Any man would do who was around and reasonably experienced. But you've a long way to go before you find out what kind of man you want and what commitment you want to make.'

He picked up a small cigar and lit it slowly, inhaling deeply before he spoke again. 'Whatever you may have thought just now, I wouldn't have allowed the situation to get out of hand. I'll permit you to experiment with me, but only so far. Beyond that neither of us will go.' He glanced at her, the cigar held lightly in his fingers, his face blank and still. 'Is that clear?'

Kate stood stunned, the red colour creeping up her neck as the humiliation registered. Beneath all the arrogance the message was clear. I don't want you. You're a child in the nursery and I'll help you grow up. But don't imagine I feel anything for you. You're a stupid, emotional adolescent, stumbling along with no idea of your own feelings.

Dear God, could he be right? She put her head back, leaning heavily against the door. Well, she had wanted to know why he married her, and now she did know. As her husband he could make love to her occasionally ... lightly, to ensure she didn't fall in love with anyone else. When he decided she was old enough or someone suitable came along, he would give her an annulment and graciously permit her to go. In the meantime she would be his prisoner with no life of her own, no friends, no Henri and no future of her own making, just the loneliness and emptiness of being his wife.

And for Blake the relationship was ideal ... perfect. Free as before his marriage to go his own way, he could end an affair that bored him by reminding the lady that ... after all, he was married.

In stunned disbelief she thought of her father. How could he have conceived anything so cold, so inhuman and cruel?

And what if she'd refused to marry Blake? Her mother said they would be penniless. But would Blake have left them to starve? And would she, herself, have minded making her own way? Other girls managed.

No, she had been weak and childish, vulnerable after her father's death, allowing her mother and Blake to persuade her. And Henri had sensed her weakness. And because of it he no longer wished to marry her.

Suddenly it seemed as though the day had been endless. She could hardly remember what she'd been like that morning, untroubled, unknowing.

'All this is not why I wanted a word with you tonight,' Blake said tonelessly. 'Tomorrow we start shooting in the studio. Please be ready.'

The heat was stifling and the lights on her hands and arms brought running rivulets of sweat into her make-up.

'Right.' Tony's voice rose above the hum of voices. 'Quiet, please. Going for a take.'

The shuffling of several dozen bodies hushed till the studio was totally silent. No one moved, and Kate felt as though everyone had stopped breathing.

'Camera.'

'Speed,' someone called. 'Slate 382 Take 3.'

'And action.' Blake's voice was low and even as he began to talk Kate through the scene. She was tense and tired. They'd been shooting for the past three days as though no life existed away from the endlessly demanding eye of the camera. She wondered how the actors and technicians could bear it week after week, the tension, the heat, the boredom between shots and the disjointed progress through the script.

'Relax your fingers . . . that's right. Now, slowly, bring up your right hand . . .' She went through it as they'd rehearsed. 'Keep the camera running,' Blake commanded. 'Now, Kate, just once more.' And finally the magic words from Blake: 'Cut and print.'

'Ease them off,' Archie called out and the lamps clicked off one by one as life returned to normal.

'Now, darling . . .' Blake put an arm round her shoulders and walked her out into the cool of early evening. They sat on the grass and he looked into her face, talking, concentrating, demanding her attention.

His 'darling' held nothing personal. He called everyone that, from actresses and hairdressers to the ravishing blonde continuity girl always at his side, gazing adoringly up into his face. All in all, Kate thought in dispassionate appraisal of his dark magnetic looks, he used everyone. She wondered if using people to get what he wanted on the screen had become so much a part of him that he couldn't stop doing it in his private life.

'Kate, are you listening?' he asked impatiently.

'I'm sorry.'

'Yes, well, there's not much time. And time costs money. We have to finish in the studio tonight. So do you think you could give me your attention for a few more minutes?' he drawled sarcastically.

'I'm tired,' she said evenly, 'and I'm not an actress.'

'I'm well aware of it,' he answered curtly.

'You wanted me to do this,' she commented tartly, 'you may remember I refused.'

He jumped to his feet in one lithe movement and walked away from her to stand staring out across the bay, and Kate wondered what he was thinking. When he came back a moment later she saw the lines of tiredness etched into his face. He bent down and took her hands, lifting her to her feet, holding her close and looking down into her eyes.

'Just one more,' he said quietly, 'I know how tired you are, but this is the last shot.' He leaned forward and kissed her softly on the mouth. 'Come,' he said, 'let's walk.'

Kate felt the tears prick her lids, her anger

dissolving at the gentle caress. Holding hands they walked to the headland, the breeze cool against their faces, the sun muted, sinking slowly, throwing long black shadows across the rocks and into the bay below. Kate felt a sudden release, a strange uplifting happiness. For once Blake's mood and her own seemed in tune, the quiet beauty all round enveloping them both.

'I want you to destroy the bust,' Blake said softly.

'No ... oh, no, I can't. Please don't ask me, Blake ...'

'Let me finish, love,' he interrupted. 'Yesterday we tried it with Blanche on a dummy, and it didn't work. She doesn't know how to break up the clay. You do.' He turned to face her. 'Look at me,' he commanded, and she lifted her eyes to his face. 'Laura's been abandoned.' Blake's look was intent, no mockery now in his eyes.

'She feels the clay as though it's Jason's skin, his face, and she touches it as she's done in reality countless times when they've loved each other ... achingly and with the intense emotion of her memories. Suddenly she realises it's only clay, and her love turns to hate. In agony at what she's lost, she takes her revenge—not on him because he's gone—but on the likeness of him under her fingers. She tears at the bust, her hands clawing as though she's raking his skin. Finally she picks up a chisel and destroys it ... killing him.'

Blake's eyes were dark with emotion and Kate felt she was drowning in the feelings he exuded, caught up in the story he was telling. The story ... Sharply she pulled herself together. It was only a story, but he was hypnotising her, simulating Laura's emotions as though they were his own. Unable to speak, she tore her eyes from his face as he reached for her and pulled her into his arms. Bending his head to her mouth he kissed her savagely and deeply before he put her away from him and turned to walk swiftly back into the studio.

Bemused, her feelings in turmoil, she followed slowly. Inside she was taken over by technicians who touched up her make-up, pulled on the wig, looking at her critically and impersonally, smiling mechanically and making small talk at variance with their alert eyes and swiftly moving fingers, until at last she was ready.

Under the lights she looked at the finished portrait. To her tired eyes it began to dissolve. Instead of Earl's patrician head, she saw Blake's face in the clay.

Acutely aware of the silence round her, she leaned forward to the bust, her fingers tracing across the face, the brows, the broad forehead and down to the lips. Lovingly she traced their outline with light fingertips. Then she bent her head to the mouth, pressing her lips to his.

At the touch of the cold clay she became frantic, her fingers sinking into the clay, nails clawing as the truth penetrated. It wasn't Blake. It was a statue. Leaning back she looked at it, tears pouring down her face. Picking up a chisel she began to slash at the figure on the pedestal, cutting, destroying, her sobs choking her. Small moans escaped her as she slashed again and again, until the figure was reduced to a mound of clay and finally toppled with a resounding crash on to the floor.

There was a moment's complete and shattering silence as Kate came back to reality, blinking into the dazzling light, returning to life around her.

'Cut.' Blake's voice came softly. 'That's it.'
From far away Kate heard the clapping and
someone called out 'bravo', as she registered the
compliment of being applauded by technicians.
Blindly she turned to go, knowing suddenly what
had happened to her, not wanting Blake to see . . .
to guess. She pushed open the door and ran down
to the house, leaving behind her voices questioning and concerned.

Blake caught up with her in the hall, his hands
on her arms as he pulled her back against him.

'It's all right, little one, you were wonderful,'
he murmured into her hair.

'Please, Blake, let me go. I'm tired,' she
whispered and pulled away, suddenly terrified of
his touch. She ran upstairs without looking back.
In her bedroom, with the door locked, she flung
herself on to the bed, digging her fingers into the
silk cover, her face buried in the pillows as she
tried to stifle the cries that tore at her throat,
giving way to the anguish that rocked her. On
and on she wept, till there was nothing left and
she felt drained and empty.

Slowly she got up and walked unsteadily to the
window, opening the shutters to the night air, her
eyes unseeing on the black horizon.

Below everything was silent and still. The unit
must have packed and gone. She only hoped
Blake had gone with them. Blake.

Could it be true or had she imagined it? Could
she have fallen in love with him? Or was it all
part of the strange tortuous magic of his make-
believe film world, a world she had shared with
him so intimately in the past week?

During the day, working at his side, she had
watched him, searching for the thoughts behind

that smooth, suave public image. The heat and
confinement with so many people in such a small
space bred short tempers and brought tantrums
from Blanche if Blake's attention strayed from
her. But he never lost his cool or raised his voice.

At night when everyone had gone he sank into
exhaustion, his face darkened into lines of fatigue,
his body drained. And for an hour he sat, eyes
closed, completely silent, regenerating his energy
before he began the evening's work preparing for
the following day's shots. And slowly Kate began
to understand his need for privacy and seclusion.

She leaned forward out of the window.
Immediately below on the terrace she could make
out the glow of a cigar, a figure lying on a
lounger. Blake.

Hurriedly she closed the shutters, stripping off
her clothes and diving into bed. But her mind
wouldn't let go, refusing her the sleep she craved.
Memories and thoughts jostled in her head and
under her closed lids. Her clock registered
midnight when she heard his car. Briefly the
headlights travelled across her ceiling before it
roared away into the distance.

Fiona, she thought painfully, before she turned
her face into the pillow and wept again, crying
weakly until she finally drifted into sleep.

CHAPTER SEVEN

KATE sat on the bed, miserably conscious of her own indecision. From downstairs she could hear the party in progress, and still she wasn't sure if she could go through with it. The party had been a surprise that had awaited her at breakfast that morning.

Expecting an empty house as usual, she had been amazed to find Blake on the terrace. The table was laid festively with a cake, its eighteen candles lit, round it presents and post from London.

'Many happy returns.' Blake smiled for once without mockery. She blushed, her eyes on the crisp short-sleeved safari shirt, the soft dusting of black hairs on the tanned skin of his arms. As she stood uncertain, he pulled out a chair.

'Aren't you going to open everything?'

There was a card from Paris, some home-made chocolates from Annabelle and a glittering package from Blake. She looked at him rather shyly and he nodded encouragement.

'See if you like it. It's a birthday present and a thank you for the film. I'm grateful and appreciative,' he said roughly.

She flushed at his words and unwrapped the present. Inside the black velvet box was a three strand pearl choker necklace, the faintly pink glow of real pearls gleaming against the brilliant blue square sapphire in the centre.

'Oh, Blake, it's fabulous,' she breathed, 'just

beautiful. Thank you.' She smiled up into his face.

'Glad you like it,' he commented casually and reached for his coffee. 'Tonight we're giving a party,' he announced next. 'It'll be your birthday party and the usual end of location "do" with the crew and some locals.'

'How lovely,' she sparkled.

'That's the first smile I've had out of you in weeks,' he observed drily, his eyes rather intent on her face. 'I've another present which I think you'll enjoy even more,' he went on quietly.

Abruptly he put down his cup and got up, standing with his back to her, his hands deep in his pockets while Kate waited with a strange sense of foreboding.

'I've been worried about you,' he said tightly. 'Because you're so mature in some ways I tend to forget how much living you have to do before ...' He raked his hand through his hair impatiently before he turned back to face her, his gaze fixed on a point above her head as she watched apprehensively. 'I've decided to call it a day, Kate. I'm setting you free,' he said roughly, 'you can have your annulment.'

Kate tried to focus her mind, but her eyes mirrored the shock into which he had flung her. Too late. That was her only coherent thought. A month ago, she would have been overjoyed, but now she felt as though her world was falling apart. Had he guessed how she felt about him? Was that why he wanted her gone? Dear God, she hoped not. He must never know what she felt at being discarded with all the others who had come up against his indifference.

'I've made arrangements for you to stay with

friends in London until the beginning of the term
for your art school,' he said dully. 'Then you're
booked into a student house.'

Kate looked down at her tightly clenched
hands. 'When do I go?'

'Whenever you wish,' he replied tautly. 'If you
want to stay here, have a holiday . . . ask a friend,
perhaps . . .?' The impersonal concern hit her
more forcibly than open hostility would have
done, and she could feel depression and desolation
flooding through her.

'So,' she ventured, lifting her head, eyes veiled
carefully, 'am I free to marry?'

'No,' he bit out, 'not yet. It will take time to
sort out the legalities,' he went on more quietly.
He lowered his eyes to her face, staring intently.
'Are you planning to be married?'

She didn't answer directly. 'Will I see you in
London?' she asked.

'No,' he repeated harshly, 'I've decided to edit
the film in Paris. But if you want me to make any
arrangements for your holidays . . . Christmas,
please get in touch. Sherwood will always know
where to find me. He'll be handling your end of
the annulment.'

Blindly Kate watched the early morning sun
reflected in the water of the pool, its rays dazzling
the eyes. If only she knew more about men, she
thought dismally, she might be able to handle
this instead of sitting like an idiot asking stupid
questions. She wanted to scream at him: take me,
please take me; I don't care about anything else,
just keep me with you, even if it's only for a
while.

But she said nothing, rooted to her chair, her
eyes riveted to the necklace, the sapphire glinting

in the sun. A goodbye present, she thought cynically, not even for services rendered.

'You don't seem overjoyed,' he said suddenly.

'It's rather a surprise. I'm just taking it in.'

'Your fees will be paid directly to college and your expenses into your bank. Sherwood will help if there are any problems.'

Well, that was that. He'd obviously thought it all out. This was no decision made on the spur of the moment, and suddenly she wished he'd go. She didn't want to see him again and wondered if she could slip away before the party.

'You'll need a new dress for tonight,' he said next. 'I've arranged for a car to take you into Cannes. I have accounts at several boutiques.'

I bet you have, she thought bitterly. At least he always ran true to form.

He straightened. 'You don't seem to have anything to say,' he remarked coolly, 'so I'll be off.'

Turning away he strode swiftly round the side of the house and out of sight.

Kate stood up and took a last look at herself in the full-length mirror. For the hundredth time she wondered what devil had prompted her to buy the dress. Firmly declining the chauffeur's offer to stop at various boutiques in Cannes, she had wandered round on her own. Having spent nothing of the lavish allowance Blake had been paying into her account, she determined to blow the lot on a dress.

Finally, footsore and hot, she found it. In a tiny back street, the low window held only the one dress, and she knew her search was at an end. The elderly lady inside had been surprised at her choice and tried to dissuade her.

'It is ... how you say, for the older, more sophisticated *femme*' she stressed, 'and *mademoiselle* is so *jeune fille*, so *ravissante*, she does not need the ... er ... exposure.'

Kate knew exactly what she meant, but insisted she try it on. It was black satin and clung to her figure like a sensuous nightdress, the skirt swirling decorously round her ankles, the top daring and showy. Cut like a pinafore, two wide bands of the material crossed diagonally over her breasts and across her shoulders down to the waist at the back, leaving bare skin exposed under her arms to the waist, the shape of her breasts and nipples clearly outlined under the tight satin.

'I'll take it,' she said casually without wincing at the outrageous price, and added strappy sandals to complete the outfit.

The villa was all bustle and activity in preparation for the evening, and she slipped up to her room unobserved, hanging the dress away before returning downstairs for a solitary swim.

Lying on her back in the pool she made her plans. She would not slink out of Blake's life. She would go, flags flying. It was time a woman showed him some spirit. All she wanted was one look from him to show he desired her. After that she would leave him without a backward glance.

There would be no art school and for this she was briefly regretful. But she wouldn't permit Blake to finance her after their marriage ended. She would earn her own living and move into a world where he couldn't find her. That meant no Paris, and no Henri who seemed suddenly a rather distant first love, a spurt of emotion she could barely recall.

But the euphoria of the pool hadn't lasted. And

now she had to decide. It would take only a moment to strip off the black satin and slip into one of her lovely Paris gowns. No, she thought rebelliously, she was no longer a child. She would show him she was not the stupid adolescent he thought her to be.

Resisting the temptation to put a silk shawl round her shoulders, she walked downstairs hoping no one would see the pounding of her pulses or hear the loud thumping of her heart.

Downstairs the place was packed. Kate had never seen so many people crowded together, and the noise was deafening. She smiled grimly. It was unlikely Blake would even find her, and there was no way he could evince sudden desperate lust in all this heat and noise.

'Kate?' She turned to see Tony making his way towards her. 'There you are,' he said absently, his eyes roving over her, expertly appraising.

'Hello,' she responded nervously.

'Wow!' He breathed hard. 'To hell with drinking.' He put his glass down and slung an arm round her. 'Let's dance.'

'Here?' She was incredulous. 'There's no room.'

'Plenty of room for my kind of dancing,' he said mischievously, and Kate realised her evening was under way. Within moments she could feel his hand inside her dress on her back as his steps slowed and he pressed himself against her. She wriggled away from him, but he held her tightly and she stopped fighting. At least he didn't regard her as an idiot adolescent. He was treating her like a grown woman and she liked it . . . for the moment anyway, she thought uneasily, wondering where Blake might be.

And then she forgot Blake and the dress as they emerged on to the dance floor and she discovered Tony was a superb dancer. They whirled to the fast beat of the music, Kate's hair flying, their steps in unison, her feet barely touching the ground as Tony held her and she felt a rising exhilaration.

The music finished on a thunderous climax of drums and brass as they stopped with a flourish, Tony clasping her tightly, one hand still inside her dress.

Kate threw her head back and looked up. Everyone seemed to be watching them as they stood alone in the small area of floor cleared for dancing. Slightly bemused she looked round the staring faces to find Blake's eyes on her. They were blazing, but not with the desire she had planned. His face was furious, his mouth grim, the eyes cold with contempt. He was standing with his arm round Paddy, the continuity girl who was dressed in a sleek, skin-tight silver boiler suit, the metallic material almost totally transparent, revealing clearly she was wearing only a g-string underneath.

At the sight of that sophisticated sexy outfit, Kate's confidence shrivelled, and the bubble burst with hideous mockery, the whole childish fantasy staring her in the face. There was no way Blake wanted her sexually. The icy disdain in his eyes only confirmed his total indifference. And now all she wanted was to run away from him . . . from them all. Instead she turned to the bemused Tony, her eyes sparkling, her voice light and gay.

'Shall we get some air?'

Turning blindly she headed for the terrace as Tony clung to her arm and followed obediently.

Once outside she breathed deeply and walked away from him down the steps to the pool.

'Mm ... coming with you,' he muttered fiercely, the sudden cool night air sobering him. He steadied and grabbed her, pushing her against one of the vine-covered pillars. She could feel the prickle of leaves scratch her back as his body pressed into her, his fingers groping clumsily under her dress. She reacted sharply.

'Let go, Tony, please.'

'With that dress, my lovely, you're asking for it,' he mumbled, 'and I got there first.'

Disgusted with him as much as with herself, she tried to push him away, but he was unexpectedly stronger than she anticipated. His mouth loose and moist, pressed against her closed lips, and she could smell the drink on his breath. Suddenly she felt very much alone with him.

'Come on, gorgeous, give,' he muttered thickly, his mouth trailing down her throat. 'There can't be much you don't know, married to Blake.'

She beat her fists against him and kicked his shins with the heel of her sandal, writhing to get away.

'What's the matter?' His voice was slurred. 'Scared he'll find us? Well, he won't. Too busy with little Paddy. Been with willing little Paddy all evening. She's hungry for him,' he leered at her, laughing lightly, 'and little Paddy always gets what she wants.'

Kate felt sickened and gave him a push with all her strength. For a moment he staggered backwards and she headed away from him towards the house, relief flooding through her. But then he caught her from behind. She heard her skirt rip as he pulled her back, and this time he gripped her in an iron hold.

'So, you're a tease, are you?'

'Please, Tony, let me go,' she pleaded, 'someone will see us.'

'So what? Everyone else is at it . . . always is at these parties.'

He bent his head to her breast and she began to feel faint with revulsion, leaning giddily against him, fearful she would fall. As his lips touched her breast she screamed. And suddenly she was free, watching bemused as Blake hauled Tony away from her. Walking deliberately to the edge of the pool, Blake dropped him into the water. Without a backward glance he strode back to her.

She was breathing heavily, reaction setting in as she leaned against the pillar behind her, the faintness slowly receding, the tremors still shaking her body. Music and voices reached them indistinctly from the house, but the silence round the pool was disturbed only by the spluttering from the sobering Tony coming up for air.

Without a word Blake reached for her arm and gripped it hard as he pulled her along behind him, part of her skirt trailing. She knew better than to ask questions as he dragged her away from the party, round the house into a side entrance. He took the back stairs two at a time, and she tripped across the hem of her skirt, falling heavily against the banisters. He swore savagely and bent to pick her up, carrying her to her bedroom.

Dumping her carelessly on to the bed he strode to the door, and she hoped fervently he'd leave her alone. Instead he turned the key in the lock and stood looking across at her. He hadn't

switched on the light and she couldn't see his
eyes in the moonlight filtering through the open
windows, but she sensed his anger in the cruel
curve of the mouth and the grim set of his jaw.

When he didn't speak, she moved, getting up
slowly. She wasn't going to lie there cowering
before him like some criminal. If he wanted a
fight, she'd give him one. Still he didn't say
anything. Instead he walked firmly towards her
and she shrank back against the edge of the bed,
suddenly fearful of his intentions. He moved past
her as though she wasn't there and opened her
wardrobe. Picking out the nearest long dress he
threw it across the bed.

'Put it on,' he snapped.

'No, Blake, I'm not coming down again. I'm
going to bed.'

'You'll go to bed when I'm good and ready to
let you. Now get into that.'

He walked up to her, standing so close she could
smell his cologne, and she experienced a sudden
longing to throw herself into his arms, to feel the
touch of his hands and mouth against her face.

'No.' She turned her back to him and heard the
rasp of his indrawn breath before he gripped her
shoulders, swinging her round to face him.

'What the bloody hell did you think you were
doing?' She could see his eyes now, hard and
blazing, the lids lifted.

'By the time you came down they were all
high.' His fingers bit into her flesh. 'I don't
blame Tony one bit. I'd have done the same in
his place, and you deserved whatever he gave
you. Perhaps I should have let him get on with
what he was doing,' he snarled at her. 'Maybe
that's what you came for?'

She said nothing, looking at him wide-eyed, conscious only of the magnetism he exerted over her senses, even when he was angry with her. All she wanted was for him to take her into his arms and make love to her. Far from being frightened by his rage, she felt excited, exultant that she'd managed to rouse him.

'You still don't understand, do you?' She had never seen him so angry. 'He could have taken you down to the beach and raped you, don't you realise that?' Her eyes dilated at his words. 'Oh, no.'

'Oh, yes,' he mimicked her tone. 'Was that what you wanted?' His voice dropped to low sarcasm as his anger ebbed. 'Or was it this?' he murmured, taking his hands off her arms and sliding his fingers across her back inside the dress.

She tingled at the warm sensuality of the caress, longing to arch her body to touch his. But she stood still under his touch, determined not to give him the satisfaction of knowing this was what she'd wanted all along.

'Or was it this?' he whispered, his thumbs reaching forward under the satin to touch her naked breasts, brushing lightly, tantalisingly across her nipples.

She couldn't control the shudder of desire that raced through her body. Her 'oh, no' came out in a soft moan as she leaned towards him, her eyes closed, her lips parted for his kiss.

'No, you don't, my little siren,' he laughed lightly as she opened her eyes, shocked at his rejection. 'I'll have to deny you. You'll change and come downstairs where we'll show them how deliriously happy we are together.'

'No, Blake, please don't make me.'

'But I will, child, precisely that . . . make you.'

She looked into the implacable face and saw the eyes narrowed, glinting with anger. Mutely she shook her head wishing he would just go. She was humiliated enough. He knew now how much she wanted him. Perhaps he knew also that she loved him, but he didn't care, didn't want her for himself. Her pitiful attempt at rousing his interest had failed miserably, and she should have realised at the outset how silly it was. She was not his kind, like Paddy downstairs, sophisticated, experienced and self-assured. Wildly she wished she was thirty-five and all those things, so that he would find it impossible to resist her.

'Kate I'm not asking you again. I'll dress you myself if I have to.'

'Just go away and leave me alone,' she said childishly.

'No, by God, I won't.'

He reached out and she flinched away, certain he was about to strike her. But he put his hand inside the top of her dress, and she heard the material tear as the dress fell to her feet, leaving her bare except for tiny black briefs.

She stared at him in shocked disbelief, her face and neck suffused with colour. He was blazing with rage, his mouth a thin line of fury as his eyes travelled down her body. For a moment she was sure he would take her and throw her on to the bed as passion flared in his face and the light eyes clouded. She raised her arms protectively across her breasts, afraid to move in case she triggered further violence. His chest was heaving with the effort to regain control, and she waited trembling with cold fear.

The silence seemed to last an eternity. Finally he moved. Lifting a négligé from a chair he threw it at her.

'For God's sake cover yourself,' he ground out and turned away. 'I expect you downstairs in five minutes,' he added tonelessly, and a moment later she was alone.

CHAPTER EIGHT

KATE sank back on to the bed, her body shaking, her mind unable to cope with the experience of the last few minutes. Never again would she try to play games with Blake. She hadn't the experience to cope with him. What would she have done if he had taken her there and then in the passion of his anger, without love or desire? Wearily she was aware of the minutes ticking by. She'd have to go downstairs if she wanted to avoid a repeat of what she'd just been through.

Dressed in a demure gown of floating chiffon, she was spraying perfume against her throat when she heard his step on the stairs and hurried out to meet him. He looked up at her in silence as she faltered and stopped, uncertain of his mood, ready to retreat in panic and lock her door against him if he was still angry.

And then he smiled, a crooked, mocking smile. Holding out his hand he took hers and bent his head to kiss it, his lips lingering for a moment against her wedding ring. His touch quivered up her arm, and she blushed faintly as he kept her hand firmly in his and led her downstairs.

The party was still in full swing, and Blake swung her expertly on to the dance floor, folding her close, protecting her from other couples, several the worse for drink. She moved awkwardly, tense in his arms, trying to keep her distance, but he seemed oblivious of her reluctance, moving easily and lightly, manoeuvring her towards the terrace.

'Ah, there you are.' It was Paddy, waving a champagne glass at Blake. 'I've missed you, darling,' she murmured, her face tilted provocatively to his. She turned to Kate. 'Thank you for taking care of him. I'll have him back now.'

Kate stiffened and moved away from Blake, but he gripped her hard, clamping her to his side.

'I don't think you've met my wife. Kate, this is Paddy Wentworth, my enormously efficient continuity girl.'

Kate nodded politely.

'But, dearest Blake,' Paddy said sweetly, 'we all know the child bride ... the virgin child bride,' she stressed as Kate's face flamed. 'You're too chivalrous, my angel.' She smiled brilliantly into Blake's face, her body leaning towards him. 'But then only I know how you work off the frustrations of your marriage,' she finished archly.

Kate recoiled from the venom in the other girl's face as voices round them hushed.

'Nor am I too drunk, pet, to tell you exactly what your husband likes me to do to him in bed,' she said, staring at Kate.

'My dear girl,' Blake's voice came cool and smooth. 'On the set you're invaluable, but I don't recall asking to sample other qualities.' He pushed Kate closer. 'Will you excuse us now? We're going for some air. Enjoy yourself,' he added pleasantly.

They walked outside and Kate moved away from him as the noise of voices faded behind them. 'That was cruel,' she said quietly.

'You're being naïve' he said flatly. 'You think everyone feels as you do. She tries to bed every director with whom she works. Some go to bed

with her. I don't. I never have personal relations
with my technicians, intimate or otherwise.'

Which is more than can be said of relations
with your actresses, Kate thought bitterly.

'I'm tired of words, for ever arguing, demanding, explaining,' Blake said suddenly. 'Come
here.'

He pulled her into his arms and she flinched
away, expecting more violence. But he was
gentle, drawing her to him slowly, moving with
her in time to the music. They danced round the
pool, music and laughter distantly audible as
Blake guided her, his hands warm on her back,
his cheek against her hair.

Slowly the traumas of the day began to recede,
and Kate relaxed against him.

She opened her eyes to darkness and silence. She
was lying on a lounger and someone had covered
her with a rug. As she tried to remember how she
got there, the smell of cigar smoke reached her,
and she sat up to see familiar long legs in black
evening trousers stretched out beside her.

'You fell asleep,' Blake said.

'Oh,' she leaned back again. 'Party over?'

'Everyone left some time back.'

Blake got up to stand at the railings, throwing
his cigar butt into the bushes, an arc of light
travelling briefly through the dark.

'It must be late,' Kate said nervously,
wondering why he hadn't woken her. 'I think I'll
go to bed.'

'Have you thought at all about what you're
going to do?' he asked.

She got up to stand beside him. 'I've thought
about it,' she admitted.

'And?' He turned to face her, his eyes unreadable in the dark.

'It depends.'

'On what?'

'I don't really know yet. There hasn't been time to . . .'

'What does it depend on?' he demanded harshly. 'Du Bois?'

'No.'

Suddenly she wondered if she could find the courage to tell him what she really wanted. No doubt it would bring more rejection, and she wasn't sure if she could face further hurt. For the moment she was uncertain.

'Well?'

'Some other time, Blake. It's late and I'm tired . . .' her voice tailed off.

'Does it involve me?' he asked tautly.

She moved along the terrace away from him, nervously trailing her fingers along the slats of the trellis. Could she risk telling him the truth? After all, what more could she lose? Only separation and loneliness lay ahead.

'Well?' he repeated.

'I . . .' She wetted her lips with her tongue. 'I want to . . . stay with you, Blake,' she said breathlessly. He swivelled away from her, his hands gripping the railings, his face tense and set.

'No, Kate,' he said grimly, 'we can't go on as we are. It's not possible.'

He had misunderstood her, she thought wretchedly.

'In any case you've spent the last three months trying to get away from me. Why should you suddenly want to stay?'

For a moment there was complete silence, and

Kate looked at the still figure, the granite profile, wondering if this was the end, if he would send her packing whatever her wishes.

'I want to stay with you ... to have an affair with you,' she whispered. 'I thought perhaps ... I mean, if you wanted me, for a time ... I wouldn't tie you down. I'd go when you ... tired of me.' She swallowed hard. 'I only want you to be the first,' she lied.

'No,' he thundered at her. 'Stop it, Kate.' He bent his head to look down at his hands, clenched round the wood of the railings.

So she had her answer. He didn't want her. She was too childish, too immature for him. He'd told her often enough. She was a fool.

'You don't understand,' he said tonelessly.

'It's not important,' she said quietly. 'Just forget it.'

He went on as though she had not spoken. 'You have a ... gift for the man you will ... love one day. And it's not something to hurl about indiscriminately.'

'If you mean my virginity,' she said scornfully, 'I seem to remember you had nothing but contempt for it.' She hesitated. 'The only thing I could give to the man I love would be ... myself, my love. My virginity doesn't rate very high against that,' she finished quietly.

He lifted his head and looked out into the darkness.

'And what of the fear, the hatred. What happened to all that?'

'I don't know,' she whispered. 'I just want you to make love to me.'

Slowly he turned and they looked at each other, the space between them somehow a chasm that neither could cross.

'You seem to forget we're married.' His voice was low and harsh. 'What if I decided to keep you . . . afterwards. I could refuse to let you go, deny you a divorce. Have you thought of that?'

If only you would, she thought achingly, lowering her eyes to escape his searching scrutiny.

'It doesn't seem very likely,' she murmured, her voice almost inaudible. 'You don't usually keep any woman . . . for long.'

When he didn't speak she looked at him. His body was quite still, his face curiously intent, and she wondered what he was thinking.

'Come here,' he said quietly.

Without thought, almost without volition, she moved to stand close to him, her eyes fearlessly on his face.

'Kiss me,' he demanded huskily.

For an instant, surprise held her still. Then she raised her hands to his head. Standing on tiptoe she pulled him down to her, touching the hard, cool mouth with her own, provocative, assured, her lips clinging to his, a hint of passion in the movement of her mouth, before she drew back, her fingers feathering lightly down his throat where she could feel the pulse beating rapidly. Then she released him and stepped back.

She heard his indrawn breath and dropped her eyes. She had surprised him. And he wasn't totally indifferent to her touch. As he continued to stand still, his head erect, her confidence began to fade. Why didn't he say something?

Then he reached for her and she was in his arms. His head swooped and he captured her lips in a hungry kiss, his mouth opening hers,

bruising, invading, his hand in her hair, hurting
and imprisoning her against him. For an instant
sheer terror held her. Then the sensuality of his
mouth and the heat of his body brought its own
response. She kissed him back, tentatively at
first, then passionately, opening her lips to his
tongue, her hands against his chest, fingers
searching in the open shirt for the soft dark body
hair. His lips moved to her throat, his muscled
body hardening against her softness, the heat of
his breath against her skin, and she began to
tremble with longing, digging her nails into the
skin of his chest.

At last he lifted his head and looked down into
her face, the closed eyes, the head thrown back,
her mouth, warm and passionate, raised to his.

'Blake,' she pleaded huskily, opening her eyes,
dark with the tumult of feeling he'd aroused.

Without a word he picked her up and strode
with her to the stairs.

Kate woke dreamily to an empty bed. Turning
she buried her face in the pillow at her side,
breathing in the fragrance of her husband,
remembering . . .

It had been the most surprising night of her
life. She had expected to be overwhelmed by his
expertise, his experience gained with other
women. But it hadn't turned out quite like that.
Blake had undressed her slowly, tenderly, his lips
on her skin following the movement of her hands
as he unzipped, unclipped her clothes, making
her intensely aware of the pleasure her body gave
him, to touch, to see.

Their first sight of each other had been by
starlight filtering through the shutters into the

darkness of the room, and shyness had dropped
away from her as she gazed at him. She had seen
him so often in bathing trunks, the broad
shoulders, deep chest, narrow hips and long legs.
But the power and intimacy of his naked body
was a revelation, and she felt faint with longing as
he stood before her, still as a statue.

For long moments neither moved. And slowly
Kate was gripped by doubt. Was he waiting for
her to make some move? Was he disappointed in
her? Perhaps he didn't want her after all?
Miserably she stood, apprehension cooling her
body.

And then she saw his hands clenched at his
sides, the rigid stance of his body. His lids lifted
and she saw the eyes wide open, cloudy and
glazed with passion. And suddenly she knew. He
was holding back, fearful of losing control,
hurting, possibly frightening her. She breathed
deeply, a strange confidence surging through her,
and moved towards him, so close she could hear
the thunderous beat of his heart.

'Please,' she whispered, her voice a tiny thread
in the dark, 'I'm not afraid. I want it all, Blake,
everything.' Leaning forward she touched her
fingertips lightly to the hardness of his chest and
felt him tremble, his breathing shallow, his chest
heaving. She raised her eyes to his, pleading,
darkly passionate. And the next moment he had
drawn her to him in one convulsive movement,
and their hands reached out to touch, to rouse,
their hold on each other almost violent in their
passionate longing for closeness.

And then he made love to her, his lips and
hands on her skin, caressing everywhere, rousing
her body to passionate response. Finally there

had been a moment's shocked pain. And then there was only his body taking possession of her in a storm of desire, on and on until her own body clung and responded. She heard her voice cry out, as consciousness fled and she fell exhausted into his arms, their bodies entwined in sleep.

Languorously Kate stretched, shamelessly enjoying the lethargic heaviness of her body, the new sensations of womanhood.

An hour later she walked downstairs, the comforting silence of the villa all around. A white towelling coat over her sleek striped black-and-white swimsuit, she made for the terrace, standing a moment blinded by the brilliant sunlight.

'Hello, puss.'

Bella Howard was sitting on a lounger by the pool, a tumbler of whisky by her side, a cigarette between her fingers. Kate's heart lurched unaccountably.

'Hello, mother,' she said, her voice without expression.

'You look surprised,' her mother commented lightly. 'Didn't Blake tell you I was coming?'

'No.' Kate's throat was suddenly dry. 'What brought you?'

'Well . . . your birthday of course.'

'That was yesterday,' Kate commented flatly.

'I know, darling, but I just couldn't make it earlier.' She smiled and patted the chair at her side. 'Come and sit down. Tell me all about the party.'

Kate sat down opposite, her joy and happiness seeping away as nervousness rose at her mother's appearance. As always, Bella Howard looked immaculate. A white linen shift showed up the tanned arms and slender legs. Her hair was slightly tinted with highlights, the flawless face still smooth and young.

'You look different somehow,' Bella went on sharply, 'are you properly awake?'

'I slept rather late,' Kate evaded, 'the party . . .' she ended vaguely.

'I see. Perhaps you'd better have some breakfast before we talk.'

'I expect Annabelle will bring coffee shortly,' Kate said coolly, her voice suddenly indifferent. She was no longer a child to be put down and reprimanded. She was a woman, Blake's woman and . . . for the moment, his wife. Vaguely she wondered where he was.

'When did you arrive?' she asked politely.

'I caught the night sleeper in Paris and took a car up from Marseilles.' She looked round. 'I'd forgotten how gorgeous it is down here. Paradise.' She stretched luxuriously. 'I'm going to enjoy spending the summers here.'

Kate felt a breath of cold shiver through her, and with it came a strange premonition. Dismissing it firmly as foolish she got up. 'If you'll excuse me, I'm going for a swim,' she said coolly.

'Just a minute.' Her mother's voice was sharp. Kate looked down at her. 'Why not tell me whatever it is, mother?' Kate suggested, her body tense, ready for flight. She experienced a sudden strong need for Blake, longing for his hand in hers, the reassuring sound of his deep quiet voice.

I wish you'd sit down,' Bella Howard demanded peevishly, 'you're too tall for me to squint up at you into the sun.'

Kate sat down again, her face averted, looking across the still, turquoise water of the pool.

'You should be delighted I'm here because it means you'll be free to marry your young man,' Bella Howard said in a rush. 'Blake wants me to make arrangements for you to leave.'

'When did he tell you this?' Kate demanded tightly.

'He didn't tell me,' she explained, 'we've been discussing it for some time, trying to find the best way to arrange things.'

'You've been in touch with Blake?' Kate asked evenly, her voice deliberately subdued.

'Of course,' her mother went on, 'the phone's been our only link. This last separation has been the hardest of all . . . on both of us. And last week I told him I'd had enough. It had to stop.' She flicked back her hair, eyes hidden behind huge sunglasses. 'Blake agreed your birthday was a good date on which to begin a new life . . . for all of us.'

Kate sat frozen, her face white with shock, trying to understand what her mother was telling her.

'Could you please explain?' she asked. 'I don't understand.'

'Good God, hasn't Blake told you?'

'Told me what, mother?'

'Isn't that just like a man?' Bella Howard was angry. 'All cowards at heart.' She looked away from her daughter. 'He's told you nothing?'

'No.'

'Oh dear.' She sighed extravagantly. 'I'd better explain from the beginning, I suppose. I don't really want to rake up the past . . . you're so oddly quixotic about your father. You never could see him as he really was.'

She lay back on the lounger, the huge round glasses glinting, the eyes hidden.

'It all started a long time ago . . . our love for each other. When I left your father, it was for Blake.'

'Did father know?' Kate's voice croaked ominously as her throat closed painfully.

'Oh, yes,' Bella said airily. 'He and Blake discussed it . . . all men together, you know,' she said bitterly. 'I would have to wait for Blake, they told me, till you were older, till your father could accept it, till Blake's conscience permitted. And so it began, the endless separations. Even when your father died and I was sure we could be together at last, we had to wait again. Your father forced Blake to marry you, hoping he could drive us apart, still desperately jealous.' She sighed again. 'But now at last it's over.' She laughed lightly. 'No more waiting.'

Finally Kate's mechanical responses faltered and died as her imagination escaped the icy control of her will. Terrible scenes flashed across her mind, of her mother and Blake, Blake's hands, his lips . . . Dear God, she was going to be sick. The blood drummed in her ears, and she lowered her head as faintness threatened. Longingly she wished she could black out, escape her mother's voice, the terrible words that could destroy her. And where was Blake? Why wasn't he here to stop this nightmare? To tell her mother that he loved her, Kate, deeply and passionately?

Only perhaps he didn't love her. After all she had thrown herself at him the previous night. And she had told him she wanted him to be the first. Perhaps he intended all along for her to be a one-night stand. And yet could she have imagined the passion, the tenderness, the abandoned sensuality and the closeness as he held her in sleep?

'What's the matter with you?' Her mother was on her feet looking down into her daughter's face.

'Oh, dear,' she trilled, 'don't tell me he's been playing around?' She straightened. 'He just can't leave it alone. I knew he fancied you, but I never thought he'd take it that far. Ah, well, I suppose he had to get it out of his system.'

Kate cringed at her mother's words, stinging and wounding anew. She would rather her mother fought her, lacerating her skin, than inflict the torment of knowing looks and arch sophistication.

'I'm sorry, puss, if he's hurt you, but it won't last. Others before you have agonised over his gorgeous body. They've got over it and so will you. And don't weave any fantasies about him,' she added, her voice hardening. 'You couldn't begin to live with him. You'd spend your life eaten up with jealousy till he couldn't stand the sight of you. Then, once the novelty of youth and innocence had worn off, he'd be bored out of his mind, and there'd be a messy divorce. So who needs that?'

'Because I'm older, we're well matched,' she said more quietly. 'I can satisfy him as only an experienced woman can, and when we're together he doesn't stray. And of course I don't want kids. That suits him, too.' She turned to face her daughter. 'Blake's a sophisticated man with a life of travel, success, women and money. He doesn't want a young girl who longs for home and children, all the things for which he hasn't the time or interest.'

Kate sat glued to her chair, rigid with shock. She couldn't believe it. Was it possible last night had been the joy and fulfilment she had thought, if all the time Blake loved her mother? Could he make love passionately and overwhelmingly only to forget about it the next day? Her head ached with tension, her throat tight and painful, her body frozen in the heat. But she had to be sure.

'How do I know all this is true?' she whispered hoarsely.

'Well . . .' Her mother paused, deliberating. 'Wait for him to tell you himself,' she suggested. 'He won't like it if you're still here when he gets back, but it may be best for you to hear it all from him.'

'Back?'

'Didn't you know? He's gone off to Paris . . . post production blues. When they hit him he goes off on a binge . . . women and drink. He won't be gone long . . . a few days probably.' She turned away. 'I just thought you might prefer to be gone when he returns. But there's really no need for such delicacy. After all you are of age now . . . technically.'

'How do you know he's gone to Paris?' Kate asked carefully.

'He told me at breakfast this morning,' her mother replied airily. 'Before he packed and left.'

Suddenly Kate couldn't take any more. Finding her feet, a sinking weakness in her legs, she flew along the terrace, her hair streaming out round her head, her eyes deep and dark in the pallor of her face. Breathing heavily she reached her room and locked herself in.

Slowly she sank to the floor, her strength spent as she lost consciousness.

CHAPTER NINE

IT was raining hard by the time Kate reached the West End. She hurried through to Leicester Square and looked across at the Odeon Cinema, its entrance brilliantly lit, flowers banked up the steps, the neon lights above bold and clear in the dark.

'Tonight. 7.30. Blake Templeton's THE IMAGE CRACKED. Royal Charity Première.'

Kate hesitated. She was early. Looking round she saw the snack bar. Battling her way to the counter she found a seat at the far end of the narrow room and took off her steaming coat and head scarf, sinking down on to the hard plastic bench. Cupping the hot mug with her hands she began to drink the scalding liquid.

Once again she asked herself if she should have come, knowing it would bring back memories she had tried so hard to banish. But six months was a long time, and she was no longer the frightened teenager she had been in those early days and weeks after she fled from France.

That last day she had returned to consciousness and got to her feet, easing the cramp in her legs, and looked round her room, the bed neatly made, the two pillows side by side . . .

An hour later she had left, the torn black dress tossed into the bottom of her cupboard, her wedding ring on the bedside table. Arriving in London, she had been fiercely determined to keep clear of anyone she knew, booking into a railway hotel where finally reaction had set in.

The narrow bed in that tiny impersonal room had been drenched with sweat as she began to shiver with delayed shock, the sudden devastating change of climate bringing on an attack of 'flu. For two days she lay weeping, weak and helpless, lonely and frightened. On the third morning she woke clear-eyed and dizzy with lack of food, the fever gone.

She was being stupid, she berated herself. She was young and healthy, reasonably intelligent, and there was nothing to stop her making a new life for herself.

Bathed, hair washed and starving, she had gone downstairs to the formal dining room and eaten her way through an enormous breakfast. Her bill paid, she had walked out into the station and bought a ticket on the first train leaving for out of town. Oxford. As the clerk at the ticket counter rattled off the destinations, that was the only vaguely familiar name. Two hours later she left her case at Oxford station and made her way to the employment agencies in the town, only to discover she had none of the skills needed to earn a living in the modern world.

It was at the job centre she'd been lucky. The helpful middle-aged lady was new to her post and listened sympathetically while Kate recited her schooling details. When she mentioned sculpture, the lady's eyes brightened.

'Hold on,' she stopped Kate. 'That rings bells.' She riffled through her cards and pulled one out. 'Just the thing,' she beamed, 'the school art technician's had an accident. How would you like to see the Head?'

The school building was silent and empty, and the bell brought only the caretaker to the locked iron gate.

'Sorry, miss. School holidays now,' he explained.

'Oh,' Kate turned away. 'Thank you.'

'Can I help?' he asked. 'Someone you want to see?'

'I've come about a job, but I suppose there's nothing now.'

'Teaching you mean?'

'Oh, no,' Kate smiled wanly. 'I'm from the job centre. Something about an art technician.'

'Ah, hang on a tick. I'll see if the Head's in this morning.'

Bill Harris was short, eager-eyed, brisk and busy.

'Yes, yes, come in, Miss . . .?'

'Howard,' Kate said promptly, 'Kate Howard.'

Half-an-hour later, after an inspection of the art department, Kate was offered the job, and by the end of the day she had found a modest room within walking distance of the school. She started work the following morning.

Cleaning out kilns and clearing old clay had been nothing new for her. In Paris Mademoiselle Parmentier had always insisted the girls do their own cleaning and preparatory work. At the beginning of September the school had come alive with the noise of twelve hundred children, and the work had been so gruelling, Kate had no spare moments to brood. She found she got on with most of the children in the no man's land she occupied between teachers and pupils, and the school had been in the throes of Christmas preparations on the day she had suddenly fainted.

The nurse was called and Kate taken to the medical room to lie down.

Over a cup of tea the nurse was her usual bright, practical self.

'Well, young lady, I presume you know what's wrong with you?' she asked briskly.

'Is there something wrong with me, Madge?'

'You're well on the way to having a baby,' Madge said quietly, 'you must have known.'

Kate's face paled. 'No.' The surprise was evident in her face. 'Oh, no,' she repeated painfully.

'Like that, is it?' Madge asked sympathetically. 'Well, as I tell all my girls, the first thing is to inform the father.' She looked down at Kate. 'Do you know who the father is?'

'Of course.' Kate flushed.

'Good. So tell him . . . immediately.'

'No, I couldn't. I . . . he mustn't know,' she said miserably.

'Well, it isn't any of my business,' Madge said. 'For now I'm taking you home. I've told your department head and I've your things here. So get your coat on like a good girl and let's be off.'

'Yes, of course,' Kate replied mechanically. 'I'm sorry to be a nuisance.'

'I tell you what,' Madge said lightly, 'how would you like me to come round later, have a little chat? It might help to talk to someone.'

'Thank you,' Kate stammered. 'That's good of you. Another night perhaps.' She had to be alone, to think. Blake's child. She shied away from the thought, her memories returning in a sudden rush as she put on her coat. Madge drove her home, chatting about doctors, hospitals, vitamins, and maternity benefits, just as though, Kate thought, the baby was real.

Alone at last in her little room with its low ceiling and tiny window, Kate looked out rather blindly at the beauty of Queen's College opposite. The one night with Blake and the joy she had experienced would not be the last of her marriage. Nausea rose in her throat at the thought of the child. His grandmother would also be his father's wife. It was horrible. How could she allow him to be born? And what of his future, growing up without a father, his mother in hiding keeping his birth a secret?

And then another picture flashed across her mind, of a little boy with his father's thick dark hair, the sturdy body, the grey eyes. And she knew she couldn't kill the child she and Blake had created. For him it had meant nothing that night, just a momentary impulse. If it hadn't been her that night, no doubt it would have been someone else . . . No. She shut her mind down as she'd learnt to do in the past months.

The news spread like wildfire round the staffroom at school, and Kate was surprised no one was shocked at what they assumed was her unmarried state. The advice offered came at her in a constant stream from men and women colleagues eager to permit her to profit from their experience. With the wide smocks she wore at work, the children were not aware of her pregnancy, and if her landlady noticed her growing body, she made no comment.

Kate learned to live from day to day, knowing the time would come when she'd have to live on some kind of welfare, unable to continue working. But for the moment she refused to worry, her thoughts weaving dreams round the baby she was carrying and the day she would hold it in her arms. It would be an Easter baby they told her, and she found herself counting the weeks.

It was the fourth day of the spring term, a freezing cold January afternoon, when all her dreams came to an end.

She had picked up a newly arrived lump of clay, lifting it on to the table to prepare it for an 'O' Level pottery class the following morning. An agonising pain had cramped her stomach. She had dropped the clay and fallen heavily, unable to move, the pain growing in intensity. It was the caretaker doing his rounds an hour later who had found her in the dark and called an ambulance. The next morning she had woken in hospital. A junior nurse was making her bed and informed her lightly that it had been a boy and the baby was dead.

From that day Kate had been dead herself to all feelings, living mechanically through each day, eating without taste, working without pleasure, answering automatically when anyone spoke to her and longing only for the evening and the lonely quiet of her room. She made no plans for the future, emptied her mind of all hope, only content when everyone left her alone. And eventually they did. Several at school made overtures of friendship when she first returned to work, her face stony, her eyes bleak. But she couldn't respond, didn't wish for company. Each night she sat in her room, doing nothing, thinking of nothing, unable to feel, unwilling to come back to life and the hurt that lurked, threatening to destroy her.

Kate looked at her watch. Time to go. She paid

for her coffee and stepped out into the square. The rain had stopped and a crowd had formed round the entrance of the cinema, kept back by barriers as sleek black limousines drew up and their occupants stepped on to the wide expanse of red carpet. Keeping to the back of the crowd, she stood on the pavement to one side of the entrance.

One by one they arrived, producers, backers and finally the stars. Kate's hand reached for her throat as Blake stepped out in evening dress, turning to assist his companion from the car. Blanche, in a brilliant cyclamen dress, a white ermine cape fluttering open, smiled radiantly and took Blake's hand. The cameras flashed as they walked slowly along the carpet, and Kate raised herself on tiptoe to catch a glimpse of his face. She had time only to note the mechanical smile, the hooded eyes and the achingly familiar face before he turned away.

A wave of interest swept the crowd with the next arrival, but Kate glued her eyes to the back of Blake's head as he mounted the steps. His hair had strands of white she didn't remember, but the rest was the same, the broad back, the wide shoulders taunting her with her own feelings.

At the top of the steps he suddenly turned, his body tense, his eyes searching, apparently looking directly at her. She shrank back as he continued to stare, trying to penetrate the darkness. Then someone touched his sleeve. He turned away, and a moment later was lost to view in the crowded foyer.

Kate trembled, admitting to herself why she had come, unable to keep away, desperate for even a glimpse of Blake. Hurrying round to the side entrance that would take her far away from him, she climbed the stairs and sat huddled in her coat, trembling and shivering with reaction.

As the screen credits faded everything dropped away and she lost herself in the story, recognising landmarks, reviving memories. There was the beach where she'd sketched, the studio, and Fiona who gave a superb performance of youthful arrogant sexuality, determined to take the older man from his beloved. The end titles came up and Kate slipped past the clapping audience to hurry downstairs. The heavy door swung inwards and she ran out.

The square was deserted. Head down against the wind Kate started off towards the station. And then she saw him. It was Blake. Obviously he had not been inside, and she stopped, suddenly breathless. He was walking away from her. If she waited a moment he would reach the entrance and disappear inside. But he turned abruptly, and her heart leaped with fear as he began to walk back the way he'd come, straight towards her. Should she wait, hoping he'd walk past without seeing her? Or should she run while she still had a chance to escape?

Her eyes were drawn to his face. He was looking down at the pavement, frowning slightly, a lock of hair blown across his forehead, his figure tall and broad, somehow formidable in the black cashmere coat.

And then he looked up. For a brief moment their eyes met in the damp night air, and fleetingly Kate registered the shock of recognition in his face, before she turned and ran. Dimly she heard his voice behind her, strangely hoarse. 'No, Kate . . . wait . . .'

Twisting in and out of people and cars she made it to the other side, but she could hear him behind her, his footsteps gaining. And then he closed in. Strong arms went round her, stopping and turning her. Roughly he dived down a deserted side street and dragged her into a doorway.

Pulled inside his coat, his arms holding her shivering body, she leaned weakly against him, her face pressed against the silk of his shirt where she could hear the fast beating of his heart. For a moment she stayed where she was, overwhelmed by a sense of blissful contentment, the hard warmth of his body and the familiar scent of him bringing alive her numbed and frozen senses.

'Kate?' he whispered. 'Is it really you?' His arms tightened convulsively round her back, one hand sliding under her hair, fingers probing the soft skin of her nape. 'I can't believe it,' he murmured, 'dear God . . .'

Bemused by his touch and his words, Kate wanted only to stay where she was, held by him for ever. But then she remembered. In a rush of fear and revulsion she pulled away. Nothing had changed. He was still her mother's lover. What was she doing clinging to him as though . . .

She turned to go, but he held her, hard fingers biting into her arms through the thin material of her coat.

'No,' he muttered. 'No.'

She looked up into his face, dark and shadowed above her, torn between her longing to stay and her fear of more hurt.

'I have to go, Blake, please.'

'He'll just have to wait, won't he?' he grated. 'This time there's no running away. You and I are going to talk.'

'No, Blake.' Her voice rose in fear, 'no, I can't. Please . . .'

'Blake.' The low masculine voice reached them. 'For God's sake, what are you doing?'

Kate didn't turn to face the man who was speaking.

'You have to come right away,' he went on, 'the line-up. They're waiting for you.'

'Go to hell,' Blake said succinctly.

The man tried again. 'Please, Blake, let me take care of the . . . er . . . young lady until afterwards. We can both meet you somewhere.'

'No.' Blake was shouting. 'You'll have to manage without me,' he said more quietly.

'You know that's not possible.' The man's voice was adamant.

Suddenly Kate saw her way out. From the corner of her eye she could see a taxi cruising slowly. Pushing herself away from Blake with sudden force she ran into the road.

'Taxi!' Her voice croaked, but the cab stopped and she opened the door. Behind her she could hear the two men arguing, but she didn't turn.

'Paddington,' she said quietly and climbed in. As she leaned forward to close the door, Blake loomed up and wrenched it out of her hand.

'Blake, no,' she began, but he was sitting beside her, the door slamming behind him. Through the window she could make out a thin man with a worried face as the taxi moved into the West End traffic.

'I have to catch my last train home,' Kate said quietly. 'If you want to talk I'll meet you somewhere another time.'

'Forget it,' Blake said tersely.

The driver's voice suddenly intervened. 'If this

man's bothering you, lady, I can make straight
for the nearest police station.'

'I wouldn't advise interfering between a
husband and his wife,' Blake said tightly.

Kate gave in. She knew Blake in this mood.
'Never mind.'

She sat back in the corner as Blake gave the
driver the address of his flat.

CHAPTER TEN

KATE barely recognised the penthouse apartment. A log fire burned brightly, curtains were drawn across the long windows, and spotlights gleamed on the antique furniture and hessian-covered walls.

Blake took her coat and she sat down. He came to stand in front of her, his gaze travelling from the red of her hair which she knew to be lifeless and dull, across the white pinched face with its darkly shadowed eyes and hollow cheeks, down to the small pointed breasts, the thin arms and long legs. Nothing escaped his attention, and she made no attempt to hide her gawky figure, her lack of attractions.

The silence stretched painfully and her pallor increased as he continued to stand motionless looking down at her, his eyes finally returning to her face.

'Drink?' he asked politely.

'No, thank you.'

'Coffee?'

'Yes, please.'

The meaningless phrases dropped into the tension building in the quiet room, the only sound the clink of cups and the hiss of logs spitting and crackling.

As they drank, Kate had her first real look at him. He'd taken off his jacket and tie, the black trousers of his evening suit and the white silk shirt clinging to the lean body seemingly all bone

and muscle. Her eyes lifted to his head and her
breath caught at the drawn angular planes of his
face, the heavy white of sideburns. She looked
away into the fire, schooling her face to blank
emptiness.

'What is it you want, Blake?' she asked finally.

He came to sit opposite, his eyes watchful, his
thoughts hidden.

'The truth,' he said baldly, 'why you went . . .
in your own words.'

'That's easy,' she replied flatly. 'You offered
me my freedom and I accepted. You wanted me
gone. I went.'

'But   you   refused   your   freedom.   You
wanted . . .'

'And I got what I asked for, didn't I?' she
interrupted quickly. 'You were most gallant.'

'And a disappointment from all accounts,' he
said harshly.

She raised puzzled eyes to his face. 'What . . .?'

'Perhaps it's time I improved on my performance,' he went on. He got up and came towards
her, his eyes glittering with anger as he grabbed
her roughly and pulled her towards him.

'No, Blake, please . . . you're hurting me.'

'Good,' he said coolly before he bent his head
to her face. He kissed her with savage hunger,
dragging her close, his hands and mouth probing
relentlessly, depriving her of breath. She subsided
against him, weak and giddy, feeling as if her
bones might crack in the ruthless grip of his
fingers. But still the kiss went on, and slowly she
began to respond to the heat of his mouth, the
touch of his body, until she was clinging to him,
her hands caressing the taut muscles of his
shoulders, her body bending to his.

It was Blake who finally pulled away. She dropped back on to her chair, heartbeat accelerated, her skin electrically charged. Vainly she tried to marshal her thoughts as self-disgust washed through her. Instead of rejecting his touch, knowing of his relationship with her mother, she had responded to him wildly, showing him all too clearly how easily he could take her whenever he wished.

From the other side of the room she heard his voice, low and harsh.

'What's happened to you, Kate? You're nothing but skin and bone.'

'I . . . I've been ill.'

He turned to her. 'What was it?'

'It's all over now,' she evaded his question.

'I want an answer, Kate.'

'I lost my baby . . . at five months,' she whispered.

The hiss of his indrawn breath was strident in the quiet room.

'Was it mine?' he demanded tautly.

She stared at him in total disbelief, to find his eyes on her, dark and cloudy, the face strained and curiously pale.

'Yes,' she said quietly.

'And you killed it,' he said flatly.

'No!' she cried out. 'I wanted to die too, when they told me.' Weakly she subsided on to the carpet in front of the fire, hugging her arms round her body as she remembered the impersonal hospital ward, the empty flatness of her own body and the anguish of her loss.

'If it wasn't an abortion, what happened?'

'I . . . I had an accident.'

'And why?' Blake was suddenly shouting.

'Could it be because you weren't with me where you belonged, where you would have had the care you needed?' He came closer, the firelight flickering across his face, his rage spilling over her.

'That night . . . you told me you loved me,' he ground out. 'What sort of love is it that denies me the right to know my own child, to watch it grow in your body?' He bent down and hauled her to her feet, his hands tight on her arms. 'What are you anyway, some lunatic adolescent or just a cold bitch without any feelings?'

Her weakness fled at his anger, his unjust accusations.

'So I should have stayed, should I?' Her voice rose as she taunted him. 'And what if the baby had lived to be the little boy of my dreams, how would I have explained to him that his grandmother was also his father's wife? How does that rate in your high moral code?'

His hands dropped away from her and she turned to pick up her coat.

'Just a moment.'

'No, Blake, I'm leaving,' she said dully.

He walked to the door and locked it, pocketing the key, and reminding her of another night when he had locked them both into her room and she had discovered how the violence in him could erupt and hurt.

'We seem to be communicating at last,' he said quietly, all trace of anger suddenly gone. He took her coat from her nervous fingers, flinging it across a chair before he walked to his desk to sit down behind it and lighting a cheroot.

'I'd like you to go through it now . . . from the beginning.'

'If I do that, will you let me go?'

'I'm promising nothing. But I want to hear it all . . . everything. If it takes the rest of the night,' he said grimly.

Kate recognised the implacable tone only too well. Blake never made idle threats. Turning her back to him she began, slowly.

'That morning . . . when I came downstairs, Mother was there. She assumed I knew, that you'd told me . . .'

'Told you what?' he interrupted.

'This is silly, Blake,' she said sharply, turning to face him. 'Why are you putting me through this? You know it all . . . planned it with my mother.'

'Keep talking,' he said calmly.

She turned away again.

'Mother told me you were planning to marry her, that you'd been . . . lovers for years and you'd only stayed apart for my father's sake.' Kate swallowed. 'She said you'd gone to . . . Paris to . . . unwind, and wanted me gone before you got back.'

'Go on,' he commanded curtly.

'That's all,' she said dully.

'Was there nothing about your father, our marriage?' His voice was hard.

'Yes,' she admitted quietly. 'Father wanted you to marry me so that you couldn't . . . marry her.'

There was silence as Kate finished.

'Tell me,' he said at last, his voice even, 'did you believe her?'

'Believe her?' She swung round to face him. 'Of course. Why should she lie to me?'

'So what happened next?' The quiet voice was suddenly menacing. He got up and came towards her, halting in the middle of the room, his eyes searching her face.

'I . . . left.'

'So you did,' he drawled. 'Your mother whom you've hated since childhood and who's always disliked you, tells you a story about your husband. And what do you do? Do you tell her to go to hell, to mind her own business? Do you ask your husband if it's true? Oh, no. You run. You flee for your life, shocked, disgusted, outraged.' He was snarling now, his face twisted with rage, and she flinched from the blazing anger in his eyes.

'So what was it that night we spent together? Some kind of adolescent fantasy about a father figure? No doubt that's what the experts would call it. Or were you in need of a stud? That could have been arranged.' There was a stunned silence as he finished and Kate felt bludgeoned by his passion.

'Are you telling me it wasn't true . . . all the things my mother told me?' she demanded.

'Here it comes,' he said smoothly, 'the question that is six months and ten days too late.'

Kate stared at him. Was it possible she had been wrong to believe her mother? But he had not been there to ask. If not to Paris, where had he gone? Without telling her. How often in the past months she had wondered if she should have stayed, waited for him, confront him with a demand for the truth. But she had been sure her mother had told her only what Blake wanted her to know. Still Blake didn't speak.

'For God's sake, why can't you tell me if it's true or not?'

'Because love is a two-sided coin, and one side is called trust. Last year you didn't trust me

enough to ask me if your mother's accusations
were true. Why should I now satisfy your
curiosity?'

'Curiosity?' Kate echoed. 'Is that what you
think I feel?'

'And if I told you now, would you trust me in
the same way?'

'What do you mean?'

'Could you promise to believe my explanations,
completely, taking me on trust for better or worse
. . . as I am, without question?'

Kate looked at him, the compressed lips, the
hooded, secretive eyes. Would she believe him?
Could she promise never to have doubts in the
future?

'Precisely, my love,' he said quietly into the
silence.

She was beginning to feel faint with exhaustion
and confusion. What did Blake want of her?
What did he expect? And why had she been
brought here? Was he putting her through some
kind of test because he didn't trust her, didn't
believe she loved him? Or was it just another of
his games, his bid to control people and their
emotions?

'So, if you don't trust me or believe me, why
am I here?' she asked wearily.

He sat down and faced away from her into the
fire.

'You may remember that last night in France I
warned you. If we did as you wanted and became
lovers, I would have the power to keep you to
your marriage vows.' He paused. 'You may not
have enjoyed your first taste of married intimacy,'
he went on harshly, 'but nevertheless we are now
fully married.'

'So we have to get a divorce instead of an annulment.'

'On the contrary. Our marriage is about to start.'

'I don't understand,' she whispered.

'It's quite simple. You will live here with me as my wife . . . publicly and . . . privately if I wish it. You will run my home, entertain my friends, sharing my life in full. And you will behave and dress accordingly.'

'You can't be serious,' she said fiercely. 'Stay with you, share you with my mother? I don't play that sort of game.'

'I assure you it's no game,' he said coldly.

Kate sat silent and unmoving. She couldn't do it . . . stay with him on his terms. His obvious intention to continue to see her mother while their marriage went on . . . it was all too much.

And she had changed. She was no longer the cowed schoolgirl he had married, tossing about on a sea of emotion. The past months had taught her just how deeply she did love him. During the time they'd been apart there had been offers . . . invitations. But she had refused them all. For her there was only Blake. He had merely to look at her across a room for her to feel vibrantly alive, responsive to him as a man. No one had ever made her feel the clamouring passion, the yearning for closeness and the longing for her love to be returned. And she had wanted his child, deeply yearned to carry it and give it birth.

No, she thought, her mind suddenly clear and uncluttered. She couldn't stay with him . . . in a continuous state of jealousy and unhappiness. She squared her shoulders, oddly resolute, and looked up to see his eyes on her.

'You can't force me to stay,' she said gravely.

'I wouldn't try,' he said softly. 'But wherever you ran I would find you. Last year I allowed your mother to persuade me to . . .' He cleared his throat. 'This time the world wouldn't be large enough to hide you. Wherever you went I'd be there . . . on your doorstep to bring you back. And don't imagine you could get at me through the courts. No magistrate or jury would hesitate once they heard how much I adored you, how I lavished every luxury on you from clothes and jewels to travel and luxury. I can be very persuasive. And once I'd explained how sadly low you were after your miscarriage, there wouldn't be a dry eye in the house.'

'You don't change, do you,' she said bitterly, 'you'd stoop to anything to get your own way.'

'It's late,' he said coldly and got up, 'so let's leave it at that, shall we? Perhaps when you know your own feelings a little better, we can discuss the matter further.' He walked to the door. 'It's time to go to bed. I'll show you your room.'

She stood up uncertainly, knowing she had missed her last train, wondering apprehensively what he meant by going to bed.

The room was beautiful. Cosy and warm, the soft lighting showed up the apple green and white of the walls and fittings, the soft velvet curtains and deep pile carpet. The huge double bed looked infinitely inviting.

'Bathroom through there,' Blake pointed. 'I'll bring you a hot drink and some sandwiches.'

'I'm not hungry,' she said politely to his retreating back.

In the bathroom with its warm fluffy towels and Dior soaps and gels, she stripped and stepped into the shower, her body relaxing under the hot spray. Wrapped in a thick towelling coat she returned to the bedroom to find a steaming mug of tea and a plate of thin smoked salmon sandwiches. Suddenly ravenous she began to eat. It seemed only moments later that Kate surfaced through the mists of sleep to find Blake beside her, his hands on her body, his lips straying softly across her face. Still drowsy with sleep she turned instinctively towards him.

'Touch me, Kate,' he murmured. 'I want your hands on me.'

Eyes closed, she reached out to run her hands across his chest, down to his waist and round his back, feeling the taut muscled skin under her fingers, desire for him rising in her body in a sweet rush of feeling.

And he caressed her, slowly, his hands on the softness of her skin, fingers teasing along her thighs, across the flatness of her stomach to the tips of her breasts where his lips teased and tormented, till she ached with pleasure.

She could feel his desire for her as urgent as her own, but he controlled his passion, guiding her fingers across his body, his mouth exploring her skin until she was thrashing beneath him, her voice crying out with wild abandon.

Finally they moved together in a frenzy of passion, and she clung to him until an explosive final thrust released her into a floating whirlpool of sensation as she subsided slowly and blissfully into sleep.

CHAPTER ELEVEN

THE alarm shrilled and Kate reached out to turn it off. She stood back from the half-finished bust, still unsure what had prompted her to start a likeness of Blake. She had captured the arrogance of the tilted head, the hard cruel mouth with its sensual promise and the broad forehead, the thick brows. Only the eyes were not quite right, somehow eluding her.

She sighed and covered it. Locking up she ran lightly downstairs and banged on the knocker of the flat below.

'It's open,' Liz called out, 'just making coffee. Come and join me.'

Kate walked through the cheerful clutter of the sitting room into the kitchen.

'Hi,' she said, 'smells good.' She breathed in the delicious aroma of coffee filtering. 'Only I can't stop.'

'Pity. Baby's asleep and I was hoping for a good natter.'

'Sorry, Liz, a heavy evening ahead.' Kate grimaced. Liz grinned back. In the faded tee-shirt and close-fitting jeans, she looked far too young to have a strapping five-week-old daughter.

Kate moved. 'I have to run. And will you tell Roger there's something wrong on the roof. It sounds like loose tiles. Been clattering all day.'

'I'll remind him. He's been under the car today, but I'll see he looks at it in the morning.'

Kate was halfway out of the door. 'You'd better hurry.' Liz came after her. 'It's going to pour any minute.'

'That's all I need,' Kate grinned, ruefully.

Although only four o'clock of a spring afternoon, the sky was dark with threatening clouds as Kate let herself out of the house into Primrose Hill. Behind the iron railings opposite the common was deserted, only one or two nannies pushing huge prams, heads down hurrying home. The first patter of raindrops hit the pavement as Kate reached the bottom of the hill and saw the taxi. She heaved a sigh of relief when it stopped, and sank thankfully into the back seat, musing again how lucky she'd been to find Roger and Liz.

The one line advertisement had been in the local paper. Rushing along to the address, she had been dismayed to see a queue of people ahead of her. Almost she had turned away. But in the end she'd accepted Liz's invitation to coffee. They'd bought the house, she explained when they were both in lucrative jobs, only to find after weeks of plastering and decorating that Liz was pregnant. Faced with the loss of one income, they'd decided to let the upstairs as a separate flat.

As soon as Kate saw the high ceiling of the airy studio with its huge skylight window facing north, she'd loved it. The small bedroom, tiny shower and kitchenette had made it perfect for her needs. But she'd not expected to get it because she'd refused woodenly all requests for references.

A week later Roger had rung to say they'd like her to take it, and by the time she'd moved her things and done some decorating, she found she had a home and friends. Roger was thoughtless, absent-minded and selfish, but he adored his wife and daughter and was blissfully content. Liz was scatty, untidy, warm and cheerful, her life built round her husband, home and baby. They accepted Kate with friendly tolerance, and within weeks Kate found in Liz a woman she could talk to.

The only subject she never discussed was her home life and her marriage, just as Blake knew nothing of her work or her second home.

Kate let herself into the flat and walked through to her bedroom. She stripped down to her underwear and lay on the bed for her exercises, stretching, clenching and relaxing every muscle from her toes right up to her eyebrows, regenerating her energy for the long evening ahead.

The annual awards ceremony of the British Academy of Film and Television Arts was being celebrated with its usual splendour at the Grosvenor House Hotel in Park Lane. An important night for show business, the cream of film and television talent would be on parade. Blake's film was nominated for two awards, one for Fiona as best supporting actress and a second for Blake himself as best director So they would be sitting in the full glare of television lights and cameras. She wondered if Blake would enjoy the limelight, forced to admit there was still much she didn't know about her husband after seven weeks of married life.

Kate had woken that first morning in her new home to find Blake had gone. A message told her he'd left for New York, but gave no indication how long he'd be away. For hours she had paced her pretty bedroom trying to contain the jealousy that plagued her. Had he gone to her mother? Was this only the beginning of the double life she might expect him to lead? She knew he had meant the threats of the previous night. So what did she really want to do?

It was Porter who helped her find a kind of stability in those early weeks. He ran Blake's London home as discreetly and efficiently as Louis and Annabelle had done in France, and he began to cosset her from the very first day. He served delicious light meals in her own sitting room, consulted her on the details of day-to-day decisions and subtly, gradually involved her in the running of the flat.

He brought in flowers which she found herself arranging in casual profusion, giving the austere elegance of the flat a touch of light and colour. He showed her the backstage details of his own job, bringing out silver and china used for entertaining, stocks of linen for guest bedrooms and taking her into the wine cellar he had converted from a walk-in pantry. It was Porter, also, who pointed out the cheque books, credit cards and club subscriptions in the drawers of the beautiful knee-hole Victorian desk in her sitting room.

She began to reacquaint herself with London, visiting old haunts from her childhood. One afternoon she walked into a Bond Street gallery and spent an hour looking at a tiny Giacometti statuette, revelling in the pleasure it gave her.

And slowly her own problems began to slide into perspective as the constant unhappiness of the past months gradually eased. She came to accept that Blake would not tell her the truth about himself and her mother. Perhaps one day she would find the courage to face her mother and demand the truth. But for the moment she chose to live from day to day, forging her own life. And whatever the future held, she had to admit she would rather be with Blake in the strange twilight world into which he had plunged her, than return to the loneliness without him.

And so she began a routine. Every morning she swam in Covent Garden in the Sanctuary, until she could manage ten lengths without palpitations. The afternoons she spent with hairdressers and in beauty salons repairing the damage of months of neglect. Gradually she lost the haggard and unkempt appearance that Blake had scrutinised that first night, and found a renewed spring in her step, hair, skin and nails once more impeccable.

Her hunt for clothes began in the *haute couture* boutiques of Dior and Yves St Laurent. She littered the flat with fashion magazines and browsed in the designer rooms at Harrods, until she knew what she wanted and began to buy.

By the time Blake returned she had found an equilibrium which helped her to cope with his demands.

He had plunged them both immediately into a full programme of social commitments. The first invitation had been dinner with friends, and Kate had been nervous. She had dressed carefully in a simple classic black silk suit with wide creamy satin lapels dipping to a low vee neckline. The evening had been surprisingly relaxed and pleasant. The following week they hosted a small

party to the National Theatre followed by dinner
at the Gavroche. Two of the guests had been
famous and considerably older, but Kate found
her Paris training helped her to entertain their
guests with quiet confidence.

And so their marriage fell into a pattern.
Blake did not go away again. He was home
most nights, and they talked lightly about her
day and the progress of his new film script.
He was attentive and courteous, bringing her
flowers, giving her exquisite items of jewellery
almost each time they went out and com-
plimenting her on her clothes, her looks and
her social success. They shared all the trappings
of married intimacy, making love each night,
and she knew his sexual passion for her
continued unabated.

But something had changed. Although he made
love with the same sensitive expertise, he never
lost control. When she responded wildly to his
lovemaking, he seemed intent on her pleasure,
but perfunctory about his own, bringing her to
fulfilment silently and with an almost grim
determination. He never again revealed the
abandoned emotion of their first night together
when he had called out her name and trembled in
her arms.

It was as though his consideration and his
unfailing courtesy became a mask he wore even in
bed. And often he would wait until he thought
her asleep before getting up to spend the rest of
the night in his own room. And gradually she felt
the strain take its toll, draining her of nervous
energy until she couldn't sleep, and during the
day her eyes showed a new weariness, a guarded
withdrawal that she could lose only when the

touch of his hands and body drove it from her consciousness.

She recognised they were drifting apart in spite of the fierce sexual passion they still shared. But the tension building between them was isolating them from each other, and Kate could see no future in their marriage. She woke each day expecting Blake to end it.

The Great Room at the Grosvenor was crowded. Huge tulip chandeliers hung above the gold damask and gleaming silver of the round tables. From the balustrade above the body of the hall Kate looked down at the glamorous women, their gowns a kaleidoscope of colour in brilliant contrast to the dark of men in evening dress.

She had chosen an oyster gown of slipper satin with deep flounces at the high neck, the colour a foil for her hair, the demure style enhancing the soft curves of her figure where the material clung.

As they walked down the elegant staircase, Blake had a hand firmly on her waist, his touch oddly possessive, and he relinquished her almost reluctantly as they reached their party. The men rose at their approach, and Kate recognised several faces. Fiona was there and Blake leaned across to kiss her lightly on the cheek. Doug Hawkins, the producer, she had met and he raised her hand briefly to his lips. As everyone settled and talk resumed her table neighbour commented to her.

'I think you and I are equally out of it,' he said. She turned to see a tall, long-legged man, with grey curly hair and amazingly brilliant blue eyes. He was sitting totally relaxed in a wheelchair drawn up to the table. 'You obviously didn't gather who I am,' he remarked next. 'Robert Carter,' he inclined his head. 'Fiona's husband.'

Kate looked at him intently, giving him her full attention.

'Last year in France we were hoping to have you visit, but it never happened, and perhaps that was just as well,' he added drily. 'I wasn't in a very good state. I've been hoping to get a chance to thank you, ever since.'

'Thank me?'

He chuckled. 'For all the times you permitted your husband to spend time with me when you were in fact on your honeymoon ... something we didn't realise.'

She looked at him, frowning slightly in bewilderment.

'I'd better explain,' he said gravely. 'Last year I had the accident that landed me in this chair, and it created havoc for us all. Fiona was just beginning to make a name for herself, and my crash landed me right in her lap. I gave her a very hard time. I couldn't seem to accept what had happened. Also our little girl was only three and didn't understand why her father couldn't run and play any more.'

He paused as waiters removed soup plates and replenished wine glasses.

'When Blake offered Fiona this part,' he went on, 'he suggested we all come over together, and he found us a house where we could be alone, away from the unit.'

He looked across at Blake, who was leaning back relaxed, slim fingers on the stem of his glass, listening to the talk around him. 'Of course, you know what a great bloke he is, but to me it came as a complete surprise. Night after night he came round and listened to me pouring out my self-pity, giving Fiona a break. And in the end it worked. Somehow I managed to think straight again, and by the time we came home we'd got it together.'

He smiled at Kate. 'You must have hated my guts, watching your husband disappear every night. Now that I've met you, I wonder Blake didn't just knock me over the head and walk away,' he laughed.

Kate blushed and looked down at her food. So Fiona and Blake had not been having an affair last year in France. In fact the young actress had been in deep trouble with a sick husband and bewildered child.

She looked across at Blake and met his eyes, gleaming mockery in their depths, as though he knew what she was thinking. Colouring faintly she looked away.

Just then the lights dimmed, indicating the main business of the evening was about to begin, and all eyes turned to the stage, where spotlights picked out the royal party arriving to take their seats. Kate could feel the excitement rippling through the hall as waiters disappeared, voices died and everyone rose to clap.

Her attention was caught by a waiter bringing a note to Blake. There was a short murmured exchange before he opened it. For a moment his face froze, and Kate wondered what it could be. Then he gestured across the table and the note was brought round to her. It was in Porter's bold, clear handwriting.

'Please ring Roger immediately. Extremely urgent. Cannot wait.'

Kate frowned. What could it mean? She would
have to find a phone. Looking up she met her
husband's eyes on her, controlled, unreadable.
Murmuring 'excuse me please', she got up and
tiptoed up the stairs to the glass doors of the exit,
scandalised eyes following her movements. Porter
was waiting in the foyer.

'The gentleman was most insistent, quite
adamant it couldn't wait.'

'That's all right, Porter. I'm sorry to have
brought you out. Thank you.'

She found the wall phone and began to dial.

'Hello?'

'Kate?' It was Roger.

'Yes, what is it?' she asked quietly.

'I don't know how to tell you,' he began rather
desperately. 'The roof ... part of the roof's
blown off.'

'Oh, no.'

'It's not good. I have the fire brigade coming, but
I'm worried about your things. The rain's pouring
in and ... well, I think you should be here.'

Oh, dear, she thought. Her pictures, ornaments,
tools ...

'All right, I'll be over as soon as I can. I have
to go home and change first.'

'Bless you, love. And I'm sorry. It's all my
fault. If I'd done something about those tiles ...'

'Yes, well, never mind. I'll see you. Take it
easy.' She hung up, thinking furiously. She
couldn't go back to Blake for explanations. She'd
have to leave a message. She turned and stiffened
in alarm. Blake was standing behind her, leaning
against the wall.

'You're not going anywhere,' he said, his voice
dangerously quiet.

'I'm sorry. I have to go. It's an emergency. I'll explain tomorrow.'

She faltered and stopped. His face was angry, his mouth compressed. 'You have commitments,' he said tightly, 'your lover will have to wait.'

'It's nothing like that,' she said quietly.

'I see. So does your Roger know you're married?' he demanded hotly.

She looked away from his face. 'He's not my Roger. And no, he doesn't.' She straightened. 'Please let me pass,' she asked calmly.

They stood facing each other, tension palpable between them. Then he moved and stupidly she began again.

'Will you apologise for me? Perhaps you could . . .' She stopped as she saw the icy contempt in his eyes. Hurriedly she brushed past him and ran across the foyer, her dress billowing out round her legs, her cape forgotten.

The house was in chaos, and Kate was appalled at the sight that met her eyes. Water was streaming into the studio from a wide hole in the ceiling, and she could hear voices from above in the attic. A fireman's ladder was leaning against the wall outside and, as she watched, a plastic sheet dropped down across the windows, shutting out the faint light from houses across the gardens.

In the sudden darkness Kate wondered if she dare turn on the light. She made for the door, intending to find Roger, when she slipped on the wet floor, falling heavily against one of the sofas. Sliding about, her face against the sodden cushions, she felt a sharp pain in her shoulder. Heaving herself up, she made her way out along

the passage where a ladder was leaning against a
square opening in the ceiling.

'Roger?' she called out.

There was a startled silence from above.

'Kate?'

'I'm here, but I can't see a thing. Can I put on
a light?'

'No, for God's sake, don't. We'll have a
blow-out.' His head appeared above her. 'Hang
on a minute. I'm just coming down.' The beam
of a flashlight appeared as Roger climbed down
to join her. 'It's good to see you, love. Come
on.'

They moved into the studio where Roger lit a
storm lamp and put it on the window sill. Kate
couldn't believe the mess that faced her. Dirty
water was everywhere. Sofas, chairs and cushions
were filthy and soaked. Her clay gleamed wetly in
the half-light and suddenly she wanted to weep,
not knowing where to begin. Roger had left
buckets to catch the worst of the water, but these
were now overflowing.

And then she caught sight of the bust of Blake.
The cloth with which she'd covered it was
clinging damply to the outline of his face, and the
sight of Blake's head in all that dirt brought on a
fit of hysterics. She began to giggle helplessly as
Roger stared in amazement.

'Cut it out, Kate,' he said roughly. 'We've got
to get cracking if you want to save any of it.'

Abruptly she stopped. 'Sorry, it isn't really
funny of course. It just seemed so truly awful for
a moment I . . . oh, well, never mind. Let's get
going.'

It was back-breaking work and went on for
hours. With mops, cloths and rags they began,

each taking half the large room. After the first hour the rain stopped and they opened the windows, releasing some of the dank, damp smell. By the time they'd finished, Kate felt her arm muscles would never be the same. But it had to be done. Had they left it till morning, the ceiling below might well have caved in.

The pale dawn was streaking the sky as Roger let Kate quietly out of the front door. They were both too tired for words, merely nodding to each other. Kate collapsed into the rear of the minicab Roger had ordered, trying hard to keep awake till she got home. In the lift she took off her sodden boots and rolled up her trousers, tiptoeing through the flat to her room. Reaching for the light switch she sensed suddenly she wasn't alone.

'So you decided not to spend the night?' Blake asked harshly.

The light came on and she looked up to see him standing by the window. His gaze swept over her, the sneering contempt changing to icy fury as he noted her tousled hair, the slack, tired pose and the damp sweater and jeans that clung to her body.

'Exhausted you, has he?' he snarled, and she recoiled from the barely leashed violence in his voice.

'Please, Blake, can we leave explanations till tomorrow?'

'I'm not interested in explanations,' he said bitingly, 'I've only waited to help myself to a little of the same your Roger enjoyed tonight.'

'No, Blake,' she said weakly, 'it wasn't anything like that, truly. I'll explain if I must, but I'm so tired.'

'You look it,' he snapped, 'but you'll have to last just a little longer I fear.'

Kate cowered away from him. His face was no longer tense and angry. It was twisted with rage, the eyes blazing with fury. She backed away in panic and tried to reach the door, but he was too quick for her. His hands gripped her arms and he threw her on to the bed, the violent impact stopping her breath, her aching shoulder ripped with pain.

'Please, Blake,' she begged, reaching out tentatively to touch his arm, moving her fingers to his hand, gently, hopefully.

'Don't touch me.'

She recoiled at the rage in his voice. Then she looked into his face pleadingly, one hand at her throat.

'Afraid, are you?' he muttered. 'Good.'

He was breathing heavily, his whole body shuddering, and suddenly she was frightened, holding her breath, her eyes huge in the white face.

Kneeling above her on the bed he unzipped her jeans and tore them off. Then he leaned forward and pulled at the flimsy briefs. His face rigid with tension, he undid his trousers. Spreading her legs and lifting her body, he forced himself into her in one swift movement.

She gasped with shock, the impact rocking her back on to the bed. He clamped his hands to her thighs, pushing and bruising as he drove for his own satisfaction.

Deep within her Kate could feel an involuntary response, a surge of desire, as she lay still, her eyes caught and held by the abandoned passion in his face. Gone was all control as he bore down relentlessly.

At last it was over. For an endless moment he looked down at her, his face twisted with bitter self-hatred, his eyes dark and bleak. Then he stood up and she fell from him, her body raw and bruised, her knees drawn up protectively.

She heard a rustle of movement as he fastened his trousers, and then there was silence.

'I hope you feel flattered,' he said at last, his voice empty and desolate. 'You're the only woman ever to make me lose control.'

CHAPTER TWELVE

KATE swung through the heavy glass doors of the Piccadilly entrance to the Ritz Hotel. The gold-and-cream mirrored hallway was crowded, ahead of her on the dais the tea ceremony of the Palm Court well under way. At Reception the hall porter smiled politely.

'Mrs Templeton? Ah, yes, madame is expecting you.'

She stepped out of the lift into the hush of the carpeted corridor and wondered again what had prompted her to accept her mother's invitation.

It was a week since the awful night of the storm, and the following morning she had moved into the studio. Roger and Liz had taken one look at her face and asked no questions, merely bringing her cups of tea as she worked to make the flat habitable. Shopping had been an ordeal, the contusions on her thighs painful when she walked. But on the third night she had finally slept, exhaustion taking over the tremors of her mind and body.

From Blake she had heard nothing.

She knocked softly on the polished wooden door, and a moment later found herself face to face with her mother. Kate's first reaction was shocked surprise. Her mother had changed. She had put on weight, and the deceptively simple dress with its ample folds couldn't hide it. The eyes, too, were different, small and oddly vulnerable in the rather puffy face with its smooth baby skin.

The two women stared at each other before Bella Howard turned and led the way through a narrow hallway to the luxurious sitting room beyond. Kate had a quick impression of high, draped windows, brocade-covered chairs and a flowered carpet, before her mother spoke.

'Shall we sit down?'

There was an awkward silence, and Kate felt ill at ease, too many painful memories between them for polite conversation.

'I'm going to be quite blunt,' her mother said stiffly, 'I asked you to come because Blake threatened to cut off my allowance unless I gave you certain information about . . . our relationship.'

In an instant Kate was on her feet. 'Forget it, Mother,' she said coldly. 'Just write it all down and send it to me. Then you can tell Blake it's been done.'

She turned to leave.

'No . . . Kate, please,' her mother said quietly, 'hear me out.'

Kate turned in surprise. She couldn't remember her mother ever calling her Kate. Standing still she waited.

'It's not . . . easy for me to talk about,' she said awkwardly. 'Perhaps I ought to tell you first that I'm married now. My husband and I live in Rio. That's why Blake couldn't find me when he came to New York some weeks back. I . . . er . . . hadn't told him I'd moved.' She looked across at Kate. 'I wish you'd come and sit down,' she said with her old petulance.

Reluctantly Kate sat down facing her mother.
Looking intently at the handkerchief she was
smoothing between nervous fingers, Bella began
to talk.

'I fell in love with Blake the first time I met
him. He was everything I'd always dreamed a
man could be, and I wanted him quite desperately. When he refused me,' she went on
tearfully, 'I felt sure he was being loyal to your
father. So I decided the only way I could have
him would be to end my marriage. When Blake
found out I'd left your father, he was horrified.
He told me he didn't love me, that he'd never
wanted me.' She gulped painfully. 'So I went
away.

'When your father was dying, I came back,
convinced Blake would relent after your father's
death and tell me he loved me after all.' She got
up, moving over to the window and looking out.
'The day before the funeral he came to see me
and told me he would be marrying you.' She
shivered. 'I went mad, begged him to give me a
chance, but it was no use. It was you he wanted
... my own daughter.' Her voice hardened.
'When he'd gone I swore I'd be revenged on him,
make him suffer as he'd hurt me.'

'And I got my chance. When we came to
Europe last year I came south to find you. That
morning ... I told you I'd seen him, and so I
had. But he didn't see me. He came running
downstairs, and for a moment I saw his face. He
looked so young and so blissfully happy, I wanted
to kill him.' She paused painfully. 'After you'd
gone, he came back,' she said slowly. 'He was
halfway up the stairs when I caught him. And I
watched him as I told him why you'd gone. I saw

the happiness die out of his face. By the time I'd finished he'd aged ten years.'

'What did you . . .'

'I never regretted it,' her mother interrupted defiantly.

'Mother, what did you tell him?' Kate insisted.

'I said you'd gone to du Bois. I told him you found his lovemaking repulsive, that his animal passion terrified you, that you couldn't bear his touch and never wanted to see him again.'

Kate went white with shock, the colour draining from her face as the room suddenly spun round her and she thought she would faint. Oh, Blake, she thought in pain, seeing her husband's face under her closed lids, knowing how deeply her mother had wounded him.

Her mother began to cry, quietly, pathetically, sniffing into her handkerchief.

'You don't understand,' she sobbed. 'I loved him. I couldn't bear to lose him.' She paused. 'I expected him to turn to me afterwards. But he didn't.'

She turned to look at Kate, her face smudged with tears.

'He went mad . . . crazy. I thought he was going to kill me. I ran away. I didn't know he could be like that . . . violent, hateful.' She shuddered.

There was a quiet knock on the door. A waiter wheeled in a trolley with tea, toast, cakes and sandwiches.

'Ah, tea,' her mother said brightly.

'I'm sorry I can't stay,' Kate said woodenly. 'Goodbye.'

Leaving the Ritz, Kate walked along Piccadilly, down Haymarket, across Trafalgar Square to the

Embankment. Crossing the river she sat down
outside the Festival Hall, the slatted bench cold
against her legs, her eyes on the turgid water of
the Thames below.

It was dusk and people were hurrying home
from work, buses and cars jamming roads and
bridges in the nightmare of traffic that strangled
London during early evening.

Slowly her agitation subsided. She supposed
she should be happy now that she knew Blake
had never loved her mother. But she couldn't
seem to feel anything. Had the past year with its
storm-tossed emotions left her drained, her
emotions dried up? Or was it the death of
her baby that had destroyed her ability to feel?

Certainly her intense hatred of her mother had
died. Seeing her again Kate had felt a curious
reversal of their roles, as though she was the older
woman and her mother the child, selfish,
wayward, heedless and cruel, to be pitied rather
than feared.

Darkness settled round her and still she sat on,
the Festival Hall behind her lit up for the
evening, voices rising briefly as people disappeared inside.

Kate was frozen when she finally reached home,
icy fingers struggling with the front door key.
The house was in darkness, and Liz's grandfather
clock chimed midnight as she crept upstairs. She
reached for the light switch and stared at the bust
of Blake. It had been pulled away from the wall
and the cover removed. Had she left it like that?

Cigar smoke drifted from the doorway to the
bedroom and she knew who it was a moment
before she turned.

'It's good,' Blake said quietly. 'Name your price.'

'It's not for sale,' she replied mechanically. 'How did you find me?'

'Through Porter. He had taken Roger's name and number the night he 'phoned. And Liz let me in when she and Roger went to bed,' he answered, the colour flushing his face as they both remembered the last time Roger's name had been mentioned between them.

He was casually dressed in brown, close-fitting leather trousers, a silk scarf knotted casually into the neck of the cashmere sweater that clung to the broad shoulders. His face was pale, the eyes ringed with weariness.

'What do you want, Blake?'

'You,' he said baldly. 'I warned you not to run, Kate.'

'I didn't run. I just left.'

'Because of what happened . . . because I raped you?' he demanded harshly.

'No.' She shook her head. 'You were angry and lost control. It happens.'

'Then why did you leave?' She watched his jaw clench. 'You love me, Kate. It's there in the portrait, all of it . . . the selfishness, the cruelty, but also the . . . love.'

'So I love you,' she said shortly. 'I'll get over it.'

He stood still, almost unnaturally motionless, and Kate wished he would go. She couldn't go on with this, her energy drained to breaking point.

'Have you seen your mother?' he asked suddenly.

'Yes.'

'So?'

'She told me . . . as you forced her to do,' she said wearily. 'But it doesn't change anything.'

'Why not? Why doesn't it?' In two strides he was at her side, his hands on her shoulders.

'Good God Kate, you're frozen, ice cold. Where have you been?'

'Out,' she said woodenly.

He dropped his hands and looked round. 'Where's the heating in this place?'

'It's controlled from the flat below and turns itself off at night.'

'Have you an electric fire?'

She shook her head and he swore softly.

'Right,' he said briskly, 'into a hot shower with you and then to bed. Come on,' he insisted when she didn't move. 'Don't just stand there. You'll catch pneumonia.'

Too tired to figure out what he was trying to do, Kate walked through to the bedroom, stripped and stepped into the shower. The hot water stung and she began to shiver as her numb frozen limbs thawed and her skin smarted under the spray. How long she stood there she didn't know, but gradually her shivering subsided and her body relaxed. Wrapping herself in a towel she returned to the bedroom to find Blake waiting.

Without a word he reached for her and began to towel her dry, his hands deft and impersonal, reviving her sluggish circulation. Suddenly she doubled up with pain as he brushed against her legs. He stopped abruptly and looked into her face.

'I'll finish now,' she said uneasily.

Slowly he took off the towel, his eyes travelling to the livid bruises on her thighs.

'Dear God, did I do that?' he demanded hoarsely.

'It looks worse than it is,' she said smiling faintly at the look of horror on his face.

He bent down and put his lips lightly against the bruises, caressing her thighs gently as the colour flamed into her face.

'Nightdress?' he asked gruffly.

She indicated the drawer and he pulled one over her head before lifting her carefully and putting her into bed. The sudden cold of the bed brought renewed shivers, and Kate lay curled under the duvet trying to get warm as he disappeared to return a moment later with a steaming mug of milk.

She sat up and drank it dutifully.

'Thank you,' she whispered, her body shaking with cold.

'This is no good,' Blake muttered and Kate watched horrified as he began to take off his clothes.

'No, Blake, please, I don't . . .'

'Stop babbling,' he said curtly. 'You've got to get warm quickly. For heavens sake don't get hysterical. I'm not going to rape you tonight.'

His brisk tone brought a fleeting smile to her face, and for a moment he stood still and looked down at her, his eyes smiling back.

How like Blake, she thought. Another man in the circumstances might baulk at the word rape. But not her husband. And then all thought faded as he slid under the duvet beside her, the single bed only just wide enough for them both. She quailed as she remembered with sudden vividness the last time they had been in bed together.

'Just forget it, Kate,' he said quietly. 'I'm only concerned with increasing your body heat.'

He curled his body round her, his arms holding

her close, and the warmth of him began to seep
into her, from the back of her neck where she
could feel his easy breathing, to her toes which
were held warmly between his feet. Slowly she
relaxed.

Kate woke to the clatter of crockery and the smell
of coffee as Blake appeared, fully dressed, a tray
in his hands.

'I see my timing's still good,' he said drily and
looked down at her, putting the tray on a chair by
the bed. Her colour rose at the look in his eyes
and she moved to get up.

'No.' He stopped her. 'Breakfast in bed this
morning.' He sat down and she saw he'd cooked
scrambled eggs and been out to buy fresh rolls,
the milky coffee was hot and strong. He tucked in
hungrily.

'Your stock of food is non-existent.' He
grinned at her. 'Porter would be horrified.'

At the mention of Porter's name her mind
returned to the previous evening and their
interrupted conversation.

'Come on, eat,' he said quietly, his face losing
its smile. They ate in silence and Kate wondered
what would happen next. Blake looked oddly
grave, the banter gone, the tension building
between them.

At last they finished and he got up to pace the
tiny bedroom.

'Kate, I . . . we must talk,' he began.

'If it's about coming back to Regent's Park, the
answer's no,' she said firmly.

He stopped pacing and stood beside the bed
looking down at her, his thoughts unreadable.
Somehow he had managed to shave, but he still

looked pale as though he hadn't slept well. As they gazed at each other she saw his eyes change, the look suddenly intent, sweeping across her face, her ruffled hair, the bare shoulders. Kate pulled the sheet up to her chin, her eyes guarded and wary.

He sat down suddenly and strong arms pulled her into his embrace as he bent his head to her mouth. She stiffened, keeping her lips firmly closed, refusing him the response leaping in her body. He lifted his hands to her head and pulled back from her lips, touching the tip of his tongue to her mouth, trailing gently, seductively. Desire for him flooded her, powerful in its immediate response to his touch as he moved his lips to her eyes, her cheeks, his mouth avidly seeking the taste of her skin. She began to tremble.

'No, Blake . . . please.'

'It's what we both want, and we're going to have it . . . now, this minute.'

Looking into his set face she knew if she gave in to him now, he would always believe he could manipulate her as he wished. And however much she loved him, she couldn't go back to the life of the past weeks, without love or commitment, living intimately . . . as strangers.

Quickly she swung her legs away from him out of the bed and rushed through into the studio, locking herself in.

There was total silence from the other room, and Kate wondered what he was doing, half-expecting . . . what? More violence as she had experienced it a week ago? She sat down, waiting, her body cold once more.

Finally she heard him move.

'All right Kate, have it your way. I'll go. But

I'll be back in fifteen minutes. You can keep me out if you wish, but we have to talk sometime, and it might as well be now. And you can relax,' he said wearily. 'That badly I don't need anyone, not even you.'

She listened to his footsteps receding down the stairs, and a moment later the front door clicked quietly.

CHAPTER THIRTEEN

THE door bell rang exactly half-an-hour later.
Blake looked cold as they stood gazing at each
other before she led the way upstairs. She had
dressed in pale blue brushed cotton jeans and an
angora sweater. In the studio she stood facing
him. He was looking over her head at the
portrait.

'Are you keeping it?'

'No.' She couldn't live with it.

'So who's bought it?'

'No one. I've donated it to be auctioned for a
children's charity. It'll go when I move.'

His eyes moved to her face. 'You're going
away?' he demanded tautly.

'Not far. I can't afford to stay here. I've found
a bedsitter.'

'What nonsense is this?' he demanded angrily.
'If you and I are separating, I will naturally . . .'

'No, Blake, you won't,' she interrupted quietly,
and sat down, her head turned away from him.
'I'd like to thank you,' she went on, 'for . . .
looking after me last night.'

'I'm your husband,' he said baldly. 'I've done
it before.'

She looked down at her hands hoping he
wouldn't rake up the past.

'You wanted to talk, Blake. What about?'

He turned away abruptly, his head bent. In the
harsh daylight she could see the shadows round
his eyes, the tufts of white in the thick brows and

the skin thinly stretched across the broad bone structure of his face.

'Whatever you may say, Kate,' he said finally, 'we both know I could have taken you just now . . . without resistance.'

'So?' She made no attempt to deny it.

'Feeling as you do,' he persisted, 'why does our marriage have to end?'

'It was always meant to be temporary. Why do you want it to continue?' Her voice was quiet and even.

'Can we leave my side for the moment and just stick to your reasons?'

'No, we can't,' she said quickly. 'That's always your response to anything personal. You want commitment from others, but you won't commit yourself. Since the day I married you I've never known what you thought or felt. I still don't know why you married me. For me marriage means sharing thoughts and feelings, hopes and dreams if you like. And I won't settle for a husband who is merely a provider, whether it's money he's offering or . . . the use of his body.' She hesitated. 'You're quite right, you could have taken me just now. You're an experienced, sensitive lover and I want you. But for me lust is not enough. And if we stayed together because of it, I'd soon grow to hate you . . . and myself. You see, I do love you,' she whispered, 'and I can't settle for what you're offering.'

She looked up at him. He was standing oddly stiff and rigid, his stance almost unnatural, unlike the usual elegance, the fluid body movements she knew so well.

'You say I'm experienced,' he said slowly, 'but I've no experience of this loving . . . sharing. I don't know how it works.' He thrust his hands deep into his trouser pockets.

'I've always kept people at a distance. Years ago I found I could travel faster alone. Women made demands, claiming time and energy, slowing me down. I'd seen too many men fall by the wayside because of wives and children, even temporary entanglements. So I chose to spend time with women who understood what I had to offer. I didn't lie or cheat, and I promised nothing I couldn't deliver. Very soon I found money and success meant I could have almost anyone I wanted ... on my own terms. And I enjoyed it. I had no deeply hidden longings for a wife and family.'

He paused while Kate sat silent. He was not telling her anything she hadn't guessed long ago.

'There were things that didn't add up, of course. The ... intimacies with women gradually became repetitive, predictable. And I began to feel a growing loneliness, sometimes most acutely when making love.' He flushed faintly. 'I could never actually sleep in the same bed with any woman. That intimacy was somehow abhorrent to me.' He turned his head to look down at her. 'You're the only woman with whom I've ever spent the night,' he added softly.

'And then one Christmas my whole carefully constructed life collapsed like a pack of cards.' He paused for a moment. 'I think you know how much I respected and admired your father. We met quite by accident at an art auction. I don't have many friends ... people close to me, and for many years your father was closer to me than any other man. And perhaps I was a little like the son he never had. Certainly he helped me unstintingly with advice, affection and support.' He began to pace again. 'That year I was spending Christmas with you both. It happened the morning we were decorating the tree. You were on the ladder trying to fix the angel to the top. We were laughing because I'd dared you to do it. Suddenly you slipped and fell. You landed on top of me and we collapsed on to the settee. I was trying to cushion your fall when I was riveted by the most urgent and intense desire I had ever known.'

He lifted his hand to thrust it through his hair.

'I was stunned, horrified, convinced my sexual appetites were becoming perverted.' He coloured deeply. 'You were just fourteen.'

Kate remembered that day. She had been embarrassed because Blake had gone quite red in the face and suddenly left.

'I visited friends with teenage daughters to test myself, but they were just children. And eventually I came back.'

He stood still, his back to the room, his eyes on the cold grey sky outside.

'Your father guessed almost at once and became deeply concerned for you. More than anyone else, he knew about my lifestyle. For years he'd watched me parade my women, until it became a joke between us. So he had good reason to worry.' He paused pensively. 'In the end he sent you away, first to boarding school and then to Paris. And all the time I was sure a short affair with you would cure me. I was convinced and so was your father that I was suffering from some kind of sexual obsession.'

He began to pace again. Kate was sitting still, her hands clasped, totally concentrated on what he was telling her, impatient for him to continue.

'While you were in Paris I came over to see you. There was never a bodyguard,' he said softly, 'it was me. And I saw you with du Bois. The jealousy I felt then was so acute that I knew my feelings for you were not infatuation. I wanted you tied to me. I couldn't bear to think of your loving another man. And I was terrified you might marry du Bois secretly and be lost to me for good.'

At last Kate looked up, her throat dry, her heart hammering.

'But your father was adamant. I was too old, too set in my ways to make you happy. You were far too young to choose a husband. And of course he was quite right.' He stopped pacing and stood still. 'Then came your father's illness and my only concern was to help him. It was almost at the very end that I saw a way to grab what I wanted,' he finished grimly, his memories absorbing him.

'I offered to waive his debts to me and to support your mother financially for the rest of her life, if he gave his consent to our marriage. The rest you know. In France I found it more and more difficult to keep away from you. When you offered me . . . what I wanted so badly, all my experience deserted me. I feared I might actually lose control and hurt you in my desperate desire for you. And then I found you passionate and responsive beyond my wildest dreams,' he said huskily. 'With you I found a joy and closeness I had never known.'

He cleared his throat. 'In the morning I left you sleeping and rushed out to re-arrange my work schedule, determined to take you on a real honeymoon, to make time to be alone with you.'

There was a long pause and Kate held her breath, willing him to go on.

'When I came back to find you gone . . . I went a little mad, and the months that followed were the worst I'd . . . ever lived through. By the time we met again, I was desperate, frantic to keep you with me. So I bullied and threatened.' He turned and looked down at her.

'And that, too, went wrong, didn't it?' he asked wryly.

As he finished Kate sat bemused, caught in a web of words and feelings that seemed to pound in her bloodstream, making it difficult to think. What did it all mean? Still she didn't really know any more of his feelings for her. There had been no mention of love. So did he expect her to return to the polite sterile marriage she had left?

Carefully avoiding his eyes, she got up and walked to the window, looking out rather blindly at the frosted lawns of the gardens below. Eventually she spoke.

'If I came back now, Blake, how long do you think it would take you to get me out of your system, to rid yourself of your sexual obsession?'

When he didn't reply, she turned round to face him. His face was strangely grey and drawn, his eyes dark with pain.

'You haven't understood have you?' he asked tautly.

'I think I have,' she said carefully, her voice controlled, her face empty of expression. 'For several years you've suffered from some kind of . . . obsession about me, and you want me back till that has run its course.'

She watched him swallow hard, his jaw clenched as he strove for control, and she waited, wondering what had made him angry. Suddenly he moved, swivelling away from her, digging his hands deep into his pockets, fists clenched.

'Are you throwing my feelings back into my face . . . to punish me?' he asked jerkily.

'What feelings, Blake?'

He turned back to her, his eyes blazing with love . . . pleading for understanding. And she smiled slowly, mistily, her vision blurred with the tears that threatened.

'Say it, Blake.'

'But you know, Kate.'

'Do I?'

'Dammit, I love you. I adore you madly . . . to distraction.'

'Oh, Blake, you fool,' she said throatily and ran into his outstretched arms. For long minutes they stood close, passions and emotions held in check, only a deep quiet thankfulness in their hold of each other.

At last Blake released her and they settled side by side, their hands linked, their faces radiant.

'Blake why didn't you tell me any of this . . . long ago?' she asked.

'How could I let you know my feelings when you told me constantly how much you were in love with another man?'

'But later . . . when I came back, that first night, why didn't you tell me the truth about . . . you and mother?'

'I knew it would be wrong,' he said painfully. 'You might have believed me, but I think there would have been doubts, always. You had to hear it from her. That's why I went to New York that first morning, to find her.'

Quietly she disentangled herself from his hold

and got up, walking away from him, avoiding his eyes as he watched her.

'Why were you so cruel to me ... about the baby, Blake? You seemed to hate me. Surely if you loved me we could have mourned the baby together.'

He didn't reply at once.

'It's difficult to explain,' he said heavily. 'I'm not sure I understand it myself. It was such a shock that you could think of having our baby without telling me. It seemed to prove somehow that you didn't love me. And I was hurt. I felt I was bleeding inside, so I lashed out at you in pain and confusion. Can you understand that and forgive me?'

She stood still, looking at him across the room, her face oddly troubled, and he got up to move to her side, taking her hands and placing them palm down against his chest.

'I'm no angel, Kate. And loving you, needing you, won't change that. I am hot-tempered. I do let my passions run away with me sometimes ... especially with you, it seems,' he mused, his eyes intent on her face. 'Perhaps in time you can change me, tame me ... make me more amenable. Mm ...' He kissed her softly. 'You see, you get under my skin. I've been scared at how close you can get to me. That makes me ... vulnerable. Do you understand, my lovely one?'

Rather wearily she leaned her head against his chest.

'But loving each other ... needing, that's still only part of it for me. What I said earlier about wanting more, that's still true. Marriage for me also means children ... a home, a future. And I know that's not in your scheme of things,' she ended miserably.

He stiffened against her. 'And who told you I didn't want a home and children?' he demanded.

She pulled back her head and looked up at him.

'I thought so,' he said after a moment. 'This is more of your mother's mischief, isn't it?'

She nodded, and he pulled her back to the sofa, sitting with his arms round her, tightly, as if he wouldn't let her go ever again.

'For a lot of men,' he explained gently, 'a home and children are of no interest until they meet the one woman with whom it suddenly becomes important. It's true I'd never thought of children till I loved you. But now it's different. I want your children, yours and mine.' He grinned down at her. 'I'd like lots of little girls that look like their mother and will adore me uncritically.' He lifted his hand to her hair, his fingers threading through the heavy silk, gently, adoringly.

'Are you really sure about all this?' she persisted. 'The past weeks you've been so ... remote, almost polite ...'

'Entirely unlike myself?' he prompted. Seeing the troubled look in her eyes he stopped teasing.

'When you came back to me, darling, you were changed beyond belief. Last year I made love to a wild, passionate girl. I wasn't prepared for a woman, oddly mature, even more desirable. I wanted to show you I could be a husband ... considerate, undemanding.' He paused awkwardly and sat up. 'But there was something else. Your mother's words still haunted me. I wasn't sure if you ...'

'No,' she interrupted passionately. 'You must have known I couldn't ...' Her voice tailed to silence.

'Not even my disgusting animal passions?' He coloured faintly, and their eyes met as both remembered the night of the storm. Reaching up she traced one finger lovingly along the thick brows, down his cheek, to his lips.

'You see,' she said shyly, 'I adore your animal passions. They're such a beautiful match for my own.'

'Mm . . .' he murmured against her finger. 'I did wonder about that when I got to New York and saw the . . . lacerations on my back.'

He smiled into her eyes, but she didn't smile back.

'And did anyone else remark on them?' she asked quietly.

'I wonder if you mean what I think,' he said slowly. 'Look at me,' he commanded, putting one hand to her chin, hard fingers turning her face to his scrutiny.

'Even now you haven't really understood how much I love you, have you?' he asked gently. 'Since our marriage there has been no one. Before that there were women, certainly. But in the last years it had become meaningless, leaving me unsatisfied and lonely.' He looked away from her. 'After we made love last year, I couldn't go to another woman.' He looked deeply into her eyes. 'So the answer is no. There was no one to see the marks on my body, and there will not be anyone . . . ever in the future.'

She reached her hands to his head, pulling him down to her, kissing him, a long lingering kiss of commitment and love, drawing her mouth away from his slowly, reluctantly.

'You see my darling one, there is one advantage in my being older than you. I can control my . . .

needs if necessary. I've never been able to talk to you about this before, but your father had another worry about our marriage. I know your mother has been ... pretty devilish in what she did to us. But in a strange way I've always pitied her.' He took her back into his arms. 'You know I loved your father dearly, but your mother didn't have an easy time with him.' She stiffened suddenly. 'Hush, let me finish. He adored her of course. But your mother was a lady with a very high sex drive, and I think your father did not share this. That's why he allowed her to have the ... odd affair before she finally left him. But you see, it made him all the more frightened for you. Because I'm so much older, he was afraid you might suffer in the same way.' The colour flushed his face, but he didn't turn away. 'That's another reason I've been ... determined you should find satisfaction with me.'

Kate said nothing, her eyes veiled as she tilted her head up at him. Then a mischievous smile lit her face.

'Do I have a strong sex drive?' she asked lightly.

'You are a minx,' her husband said severely.

'Whatever my sex drive, oh lord and master,' she teased, 'I'll have a job keeping up with you.'

'I can promise you at least that you won't be bored. You'll be far too busy. Much of the time you'll be travelling with me. You'll be running our home and having all those daughters ...'

'I insist on one son ... to adore me,' she interposed.

'Don't interrupt. I'll certainly make sure you have no time for all the men swarming round, trying to take you away from me. I knew last year Earl was only the first.'

'Rubbish,' she said scornfully, 'Earl didn't try anything of the sort.'

'Oh yes? And what was all that canoodling in the dark?'

'Blake ... last year ... why did you offer me my freedom? If you loved me why were you prepared to let me go?'

He sighed. 'You do go on, don't you? A real glutton for information. I'm not sure I like all this baring of the soul for your inspection.'

'You're not answering my question,' she pointed out.

'Mmm ... If you must know, I had no intention of letting you go. I planned to give you a breathing space, to find your feet and—hopefully—to miss me.'

'But you said we wouldn't be meeting again.'

'So I did,' he admitted cheerfully. 'And I meant it. I would probably have waited a good week before I came after you.'

'You're totally unscrupulous, aren't you?' she demanded.

'Yes, I am. And I'm glad you realise it.' He looked down into her face, suddenly serious. 'Where you're concerned, my girl, I'm not even faintly reasonable. My need of you is so strong, my love for you runs so deep, that I could never again go into the ... desert of loneliness without you. You're mine and I won't ever let you go,' he finished grimly, his arms tight round her, his face buried in her hair.

Kate sat still in his embrace, a feeling of closeness and a depth of emotion in her heart that was almost frightening in its intensity. She knew suddenly with an overwhelming sense of certainty that she belonged with him ... for always.

And then he relaxed and stood up, his face creased into a wide smile of happiness.

'Right, young lady,' he announced, 'I've had quite enough of all your questions. You talk altogether too much, and I'm not all that addicted to words. I prefer action. Come here.'

He stretched out his hands and she took them, reaching up her arms round his neck as he picked her up and carried her through into the bedroom.

ROMANCE

Variety is the spice of romance

Each month, Mills & Boon publish new romances. New stories about people falling in love. A world of variety in romance — from the best writers in the romantic world. Choose from these titles in April.

TEMPORARY HUSBAND Susan Alexander
LADY WITH A PAST Lillian Cheatham
PASSION'S VINE Elizabeth Graham
THE SIX-MONTH MARRIAGE Penny Jordan
ICE PRINCESS Madeleine Ker
ACT OF POSSESSION Anne Mather
A NO RISK AFFAIR Carole Mortimer
CAPTIVE OF FATE Margaret Pargeter
ALIEN VENGEANCE Sara Craven
THE WINGS OF LOVE Sally Wentworth

On sale where you buy paperbacks. If you require further information or have any difficulty obtaining them, write to: Mills & Boon Reader Service, PO Box 236, Thornton Road, Croydon, Surrey CR9 3RU, England.

Mills & Boon the rose of romance

Take 4
Exciting Books
Absolutely
FREE

Love, romance, intrigue... all are captured for you by Mills & Boon's top-selling authors. By becoming a regular reader of Mills & Boon's Romances you can enjoy 6 superb new titles every month plus a whole range of special benefits: your very own personal membership card, a free monthly newsletter packed with recipes, competitions, exclusive book offers and a monthly guide to the stars, plus extra bargain offers and big cash savings.

AND an Introductory FREE GIFT for YOU.
Turn over the page for details.

As a special introduction we will send you four exciting Mills & Boon Romances Free and without obligation when you complete and return this coupon.

At the same time we will reserve a subscription to Mills & Boon Reader Service for you. Every month, you will receive 6 of the very latest novels by leading Romantic Fiction authors, delivered direct to your door. You don't pay extra for delivery — postage and packing is always completely Free. There is no obligation or commitment — you can cancel your subscription at any time.

You have nothing to lose and a whole world of romance to gain.

Just fill in and post the coupon today to MILLS & BOON READER SERVICE, FREEPOST, P.O. BOX 236, CROYDON, SURREY CR9 9EL.

Please Note:- READERS IN SOUTH AFRICA write to Mills & Boon, Postbag X3010, Randburg 2125, S. Africa.

FREE BOOKS CERTIFICATE

To: Mills & Boon Reader Service, FREEPOST, P.O. Box 236, Croydon, Surrey CR9 9EL.

Please send me, free and without obligation, four Mills & Boon Romances, and reserve a Reader Service Subscription for me If I decide to subscribe I shall, from the beginning of the month following my free parcel of books, receive six new books each month for £6 60, post and packing free If I decide not to subscribe, I shall write to you within 10 days The free books are mine to keep in any case I understand that I may cancel my subscription at any time simply by writing to you I am over 18 years of age

Please write in BLOCK CAPITALS

Signature _____

Name _____

Address _____

_____ Post code _____

SEND NO MONEY — TAKE NO RISKS.

Please don't forget to include your Postcode.

Remember, postcodes speed delivery Offer applies in UK only and is not valid to present subscribers Mills & Boon reserve the right to exercise discretion in granting membership If price changes are necessary you will be notified

6R   Offer expires 31st December 1985

EP